WRITER'S CHOICE

GRAMMAR AND COMPOSITION

Lesson Plans

GLENCOE

McGraw-Hill

New York, New York   Columbus, Ohio   Mission Hills, California   Peoria, Illinois

Printed in the United States of America.

Send all inquiries to:
Glencoe/McGraw-Hill
936 Eastwind Drive
Westerville, Ohio 43081

ISBN 0–02–635535–3
Lesson Plans

 2 3 4 5 6 7 8 9–BAW–00 99 98 97 96

Contents

PART 3   RESOURCES AND SKILLS

Unit 1 Case Study: Personal Writing *SE/TWE pp. 4-9*

Teacher's Name _____ Date _____

Grade _____ Class(es) _____ Date(s)_____ M Tu W Th F

FOCUS

LESSON OVERVIEW

Objective: To explore how the writing process is applied to personal writing in a real-life situation

Skills: applying the writing process to song writing; choosing descriptive words and images

Critical Thinking: analyzing; synthesizing; classifying; recalling; relating

Speaking and Listening: note taking; informal speaking; discussing

_____ Bellringer and Grammar Link to the Bellringer, TWE p. 4

_____ Motivating Activity, TWE p. 4

TEACH

_____ Building Background, TWE p. 5

_____ Preview the Case Study, TWE p. 5

_____ Discussion Prompts, TWE pp. 6, 7

_____ Cultural Diversity, TWE p. 6

_____ Connection Across the Curriculum: Geography, TWE p. 7

Guided Practice

_____ L2, Discussion, TWE p. 8

_____ Cooperative Learning, TWE p. 8

Independent Practice

_____ *Writing Process Transparencies, 1–10 **

_____ *Cooperative Learning Activities, pp. 1–6 **

_____ *Case Studies: Writing in the Real World, pp. 1–4 **

_____ *Thinking and Study Skills, pp. 3, 5, 20, 22 **

ASSESS

_____ Responding to the Case Study, TWE p. 9

_____ Using the Grammar Link, TWE p. 9

Reteaching

_____ Reteaching activity, TWE p. 9

Enrichment

_____ Enrichment activity, TWE p. 9

CLOSE

_____ Close activity, TWE p. 9

* Teacher's Classroom Resources

• Homework Assignments •

_____

_____

_____

_____

_____

_____

_____

_____

Unit Assessment

_____ *Tests with Answer Key*
Unit 1 Choice A Test, p. 1
Unit 1 Choice B Test, p. 2
Unit 1 Composition Objective
Test, pp. 3–4

_____ *Test Generator*
Unit 1 Choice A Test
Unit 1 Choice B Test
Unit 1 Composition Objective
Test

You may wish to administer either the Unit 1 Choice A Test or the Unit 1 Choice B Test as a pretest.

1.1 Writing About What's Important to You

SE/TWE pp. 10-13

Teacher's Name _____ Date _____

Grade _____ Class(es) _____ Date(s)_____ M Tu W Th F

FOCUS
LESSON OVERVIEW
Objective: To reflect on personal values and write about them
Skills: recalling specific details of an experience; exploring thoughts and feelings; using one's own words
Critical Thinking: recalling; visualizing; relating a personal experience
Speaking and Listening: discussing

_____ Bellringer and Grammar Link to the Bellringer, TWE p. 10
_____ Motivating Activity, TWE p. 10

TEACH
Guided Practice
_____ L2, Interviewing for Details, TWE p. 11
_____ L3, Stepping into character, TWE p. 11
_____ Two-Minute Skill Drill, TWE p. 11
_____ Journal Writing Tip, TWE p. 11
_____ L2, Using the Model, TWE p. 12
_____ L1, Focusing on What's Important—and Why, TWE p. 12
_____ Enabling Strategies: LEP, TWE p. 12

Independent Practice
_____ *Fine Art Transparencies, 1–5 **
_____ *Writing Process Transparencies, 1–10 **
_____ *Writing Across the Curriculum, p. 4 **
_____ *Cooperative Learning Activities, pp. 1–6 **
_____ *Thinking and Study Skills, pp. 3–5 **
_____ *Speaking and Listening Activities, pp. 14–15 **
_____ *Composition Practice, p. 1 **

ASSESS
_____ Writing Activities Evaluation Guidelines, TWE p. 13
_____ Cross-Curricular: Art, TWE p. 13
_____ Using the Grammar Link, TWE p. 13

Reteaching
_____ *Composition Reteaching, p. 1 **

Enrichment
_____ *Composition Enrichment, p. 1 **
_____ *Fine Art Transparencies, 1–5 **
_____ About the Art, TWE p. 13

CLOSE
_____ Close activity, TWE p. 13

* Teacher's Classroom Resources

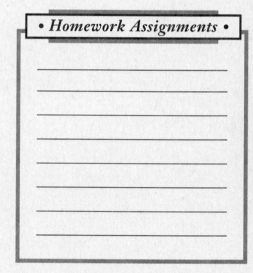

• Homework Assignments •

_____
_____
_____
_____
_____
_____
_____
_____
_____

Unit Assessment
_____ *Tests with Answer Key*
Unit 1 Choice A Test, p. 1
Unit 1 Choice B Test, p. 2
Unit 1 Composition Objective Test, pp. 3–4
_____ *Test Generator*
Unit 1 Choice A Test
Unit 1 Choice B Test
Unit 1 Composition Objective Test

You may wish to administer either the Unit 1 Choice A Test or the Unit 1 Choice B Test as a pretest.

1.2 Collecting Information *SE/TWE pp. 14-17*

Teacher's Name _____ Date _____

Grade _____ Class(es) _____ Date(s)_____ M Tu W Th F

FOCUS
LESSON OVERVIEW
Objective: To select and record information related to personal experience and interests

Skills: identifying attributes; collecting information; keeping track of information; recording information

Critical Thinking: analyzing; recalling; evaluating; summarizing

Speaking and Listening: note taking; listening

_____ Bellringer and Grammar Link to the Bellringer, TWE p. 14
_____ Motivating Activity, TWE p. 14

TEACH
Guided Practice
_____ L2, Using the Model, TWE p. 15
_____ L2, Cooperative Learning, TWE p. 15
_____ Two-Minute Skill Drill, TWE p. 15
_____ Journal Writing Tip, TWE p. 15
_____ L1, Responding to Pictures, TWE p. 16
_____ Enabling Strategies: LEP, TWE p. 16

Independent Practice
_____ *Fine Art Transparencies*, 1–5 *
_____ *Writing Process Transparencies*, 1–10 *
_____ *Writing Across the Curriculum*, p. 4 *
_____ *Cooperative Learning Activities*, pp. 1–6 *
_____ *Thinking and Study Skills*, pp. 3–4, 9 *
_____ *Speaking and Listening Activities*, pp. 14–15 *
_____ *Composition Practice*, p. 2 *

ASSESS
_____ Writing Activities Evaluation Guidelines, TWE p. 17
_____ Using the Grammar Link, TWE p. 17

Reteaching
_____ *Composition Reteaching*, p. 2 *

Enrichment
_____ *Composition Enrichment*, p. 2 *
_____ *Fine Art Transparencies*, 1–5 *

CLOSE
_____ Close activity, TWE p. 17

* Teacher's Classroom Resources

> **• Homework Assignments •**
>
> _____
> _____
> _____
> _____
> _____
> _____
> _____
> _____
> _____

1.3 Writing to Celebrate *SE/TWE pp. 18–21*

Teacher's Name _____ Date _____

Grade _____ Class(es) _____ Date(s) _____ M Tu W Th F

FOCUS
LESSON OVERVIEW
Objective: To choose main ideas to be shared in letters, invitations, and greeting cards
Skills: identifying important information; writing an invitation; writing a personal letter; recording information
Critical Thinking: analyzing; recalling; evaluating; summarizing
Speaking and Listening: speaking informally; reading aloud

_____ Bellringer and Grammar Link to the Bellringer, TWE p. 18
_____ Motivating Activity, TWE p. 18

TEACH
Guided Practice
_____ L2, Using the Model, TWE p. 19
_____ L1, Making a Bulletin Board, TWE p. 19
_____ Two–Minute Skill Drill, TWE p. 19
_____ Journal Writing Tip, TWE p. 19
_____ L2, Using the Model, TWE p. 20
_____ Enabling Strategies: LEP, TWE p. 20

Independent Practice
_____ *Fine Art Transparencies, 1–5**
_____ *Writing Process Transparencies, 1–10**
_____ *Writing Across the Curriculum, p. 4**
_____ *Cooperative Learning Activities, pp. 1–6**
_____ *Thinking and Study Skills, pp. 3–5, 15**
_____ *Speaking and Listening Activities, pp. 14–15**
_____ *Composition Practice, p. 3**

ASSESS
_____ Writing Activities Evaluation Guidelines, TWE p. 21
_____ Using the Grammar Link, TWE p. 21

Reteaching
_____ *Composition Reteaching, p. 3**

Enrichment
_____ *Composition Enrichment, p. 3**

CLOSE
_____ Close activity, TWE p. 21

* Teacher's Classroom Resources

• Homework Assignments •

_____
_____
_____
_____
_____
_____
_____
_____

1.4 Writing About Yourself *SE/TWE pp. 22–25*

Teacher's Name _____ Date _____

Grade _____ Class(es) _____ Date(s)_____ M Tu W Th F

FOCUS

LESSON OVERVIEW

Objective: To select, recall, and order information from personal experience

Skills: describing a personal experience; selecting ideas for writing a personal narrative; developing details

Critical Thinking: recalling; evaluating; synthesizing

Speaking and Listening: speaking informally

_____ Bellringer and Grammar Link to the Bellringer, TWE p. 22
_____ Motivating Activity, TWE p. 22

TEACH

Guided Practice

_____ L2, Using the Model, TWE p. 23
_____ L1, Thinking About Animals, TWE p. 23
_____ Two-Minute Skill Drill, TWE p. 23
_____ Journal Writing Tip, TWE p. 23
_____ L2, Using the Model, TWE p. 24
_____ L2, Using the Models, TWE p. 24
_____ Enabling Strategies: LEP, TWE p. 24

Independent Practice

_____ *Fine Art Transparencies,* 1–5 *
_____ *Writing Process Transparencies,* 1–10 *
_____ *Writing Across the Curriculum,* p. 5 *
_____ *Cooperative Learning Activities,* pp. 1–6 *
_____ *Thinking and Study Skills,* pp. 6–9, 11 *
_____ *Speaking and Listening Activities,* pp. 14–15 *
_____ *Composition Practice,* p. 5 *

ASSESS

_____ Writing Activities Evaluation Guidelines, TWE p. 25
_____ Cross-Curricular: Art, TWE p. 25
_____ Using the Grammar Link, TWE p. 25

Reteaching

_____ *Composition Reteaching,* p. 5 *

Enrichment

_____ *Composition Enrichment,* p. 5 *
_____ *Fine Art Transparencies,* 1–5 *
_____ About the Art, TWE p. 25

CLOSE

_____ Close activity, TWE p. 25

* Teacher's Classroom Resources

• Homework Assignments •

_____

_____

_____

_____

_____

_____

_____

_____

1.5 Responding to a Character *SE/TWE pp. 26–29*

Teacher's Name _____ Date _____

Grade _____ Class(es) _____ Date(s)_____ M Tu W Th F

FOCUS
LESSON OVERVIEW
Objective: To observe characteristics and formulate questions about characters
Skills: identifying attributes; responding to characters' actions
Critical Thinking: identifying; analyzing; evaluating
Speaking and Listening: listening to and discussing ideas in small groups

_____ Bellringer and Grammar Link to the Bellringer, TWE p. 26
_____ Motivating Activity, TWE p. 26

TEACH
Guided Practice
_____ L2, Using the Model, TWE p. 27
_____ L2, Using the Model, TWE p. 27
_____ Two-Minute Skill Drill, TWE p. 27
_____ Journal Writing Tip, TWE p. 27
_____ L2, Using the Model, TWE p. 28
_____ Enabling Strategies: LEP, TWE p. 28

Independent Practice
_____ *Fine Art Transparencies*, 1–5 *
_____ *Writing Process Transparencies*, 1–10 *
_____ *Writing Across the Curriculum*, p. 11 *
_____ *Cooperative Learning Activities*, pp. 1–6 *
_____ *Thinking and Study Skills*, pp. 3–6, 9, 22 *
_____ *Speaking and Listening Activities*, pp. 14–15 *
_____ *Composition Practice*, p. 5 *

• *Homework Assignments* •

_____

_____

_____

_____

_____

_____

_____

_____

_____

ASSESS
_____ Writing Activities Evaluation Guidelines, TWE p. 29
_____ Using the Grammar Link, TWE p. 29

Reteaching
_____ *Composition Reteaching*, p. 5 *

Enrichment
_____ *Composition Enrichment*, p. 5 *
_____ *Fine Art Transparencies*, 1–5 *
_____ About the Art, TWE p. 29

CLOSE
_____ Close activity, TWE p. 29

* Teacher's Classroom Resources

Unit 1 Writing Process in Action *SE/TWE pp. 30-33*

Teacher's Name _____ Date _____

Grade _____ Class(es) _____ Date(s)_____ M Tu W Th F

FOCUS
LESSON OVERVIEW
Objective: To explore thoughts and feelings about a special day by means of personal writing
Skills: using the five stages of the writing process: prewriting, drafting, revising, editing, and presenting
Critical Thinking: recalling; synthesizing; decision–making
Speaking and Listening: note taking; informal speaking

_____ Bellringer and Grammar Link to the Bellringer, TWE p. 30
_____ Motivating Activity, TWE p. 30

TEACH
Prewriting
_____ L2, Developing Ideas for Personal Writing, TWE p. 31

Drafting
_____ L1, Expressing Ideas in Conversation, TWE p. 31

Revising
_____ L2, Peer Editing, TWE p. 32
_____ L2, Cooperative Learning, TWE p. 32

Editing
_____ L2, Peer Editing, TWE p. 32

Presenting
_____ Presenting activity, TWE p. 32

_____ Enrichment and Extension, TWE p. 32
_____ Connections Across the Curriculum: Technology Tip, TWE p. 33
_____ Journal Writing Tip, TWE p. 33

Independent Practice
_____ *Writing Process Transparencies*, 1–10 *
_____ *Thinking and Study Skills*, pp. 3, 5, 8 *
_____ *Composition Practice*, p. 6 *
_____ **Grammar Workbook,** Lessons 93–97

ASSESS
_____ Evaluation Guidelines, TWE p. 33

Reteaching
_____ *Composition Reteaching*, p. 6 *

Enrichment
_____ *Composition Enrichment*, p. 6 *

CLOSE
_____ Close activity, TWE p. 33

* Teacher's Classroom Resources

• Homework Assignments •

_____
_____
_____
_____
_____
_____
_____
_____

Unit 1 Literature: from *The Diary of Latoya Hunter*, Latoya Hunter *SE/TWE pp. 34-39*

Teacher's Name _____ Date _____

Grade _____ Class(es) _____ Date(s)_____ M Tu W Th F

FOCUS
LESSON OVERVIEW
Objective: To follow a teenage writer on a journey of self–exploration
Skills: reading comprehension
Critical Thinking: recalling; relating main idea; summarizing; comparing
Speaking and Listening: discussing

_____ Bellringer and Motivating Activity, TWE p. 34

TEACH
Guided Practice
_____ L2, Guided Reading, TWE pp. 35–38
_____ About the Art, TWE p. 36
_____ Genre and Style, TWE p. 36
_____ Writers and Writing, TWE p. 37
_____ Cultural Diversity, TWE p. 38
_____ About the Art, TWE p. 38
_____ Enrichment and Extension, TWE p. 39

Independent Practice
_____ *Fine Art Transparencies*, 1–5 *
_____ *Speaking and Listening Activities*, pp. 14–15 *
_____ *Thinking and Study Skills*, pp. 1–6 *

ASSESS
_____ Evaluation Guidelines for Discussion, TWE p. 39

CLOSE
_____ Close activity, TWE p. 39

UNIT 1 REVIEW *p .40*
_____ Reflecting on the Unit, TWE p. 40
_____ Writing Across the Curriculum, TWE p. 40
_____ Adding to Your Portfolio, TWE p. 40
_____ Portfolio Evaluation, TWE p. 40

* Teacher's Classroom Resources

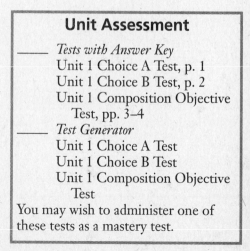

• Homework Assignments •

_____
_____
_____
_____
_____
_____
_____
_____
_____

Unit Assessment

_____ *Tests with Answer Key*
    Unit 1 Choice A Test, p. 1
    Unit 1 Choice B Test, p. 2
    Unit 1 Composition Objective
      Test, pp. 3–4
_____ *Test Generator*
    Unit 1 Choice A Test
    Unit 1 Choice B Test
    Unit 1 Composition Objective
      Test
You may wish to administer one of
these tests as a mastery test.

Unit 2 Case Study: The Writing Process *SE/TWE pp. 42-47*

Teacher's Name _____ Date _____

Grade _____ Class(es) _____ Date(s)_____ M Tu W Th F

FOCUS

LESSON OVERVIEW

Objective: To explore the use of the writing process in a real-life situation

Skills: choosing a topic; selecting effective images and details; considering the audience

Critical Thinking: evaluating; analyzing; recalling; relating; generating new information

Speaking and Listening: note taking; questioning; evaluating; discussing

_____ Bellringer and Grammar Link to the Bellringer, TWE p. 42

_____ Motivating Activity, TWE p. 42

TEACH

_____ Building Background, TWE p. 43

_____ Preview the Case Study, TWE p. 43

_____ Discussion Prompts, TWE p. 44, 45

_____ Cultural Diversity, TWE p. 44

_____ Connections Across the Curriculum: History, TWE p. 45

_____ Technology Tip, TWE p. 46

Guided Practice

_____ L2, Discussion, TWE p. 46

Independent Practice

_____ *Writing Process Transparencies*, 1–10 *

_____ *Case Studies: Writing in the Real World*, pp. 5–8 *

_____ *Cooperative Learning Activities*, pp. 7–12 *

_____ *Thinking and Study Skills*, pp. 1–5, 13, 21–22 *

ASSESS

_____ Responding to the Case Study, TWE p. 47

_____ Using the Grammar Link, TWE p. 47

Reteaching

_____ Reteaching activity, TWE p. 47

Enrichment

_____ Enrichment activity, TWE p. 47

CLOSE

_____ Close activity, TWE p. 47

* Teacher's Classroom Resources

• Homework Assignments •

_____

_____

_____

_____

_____

_____

_____

_____

Unit Assessment

_____ *Tests with Answer Key*
Unit 2 Choice A Test, p. 5
Unit 2 Choice B Test, p. 6
Unit 2 Composition Objective
Test, pp. 7–8

_____ *Test Generator*
Unit 2 Choice A Test
Unit 2 Choice B Test
Unit 2 Composition Objective
Test

You may wish to administer either the Unit 2 Choice A Test or the Unit 2 Choice B Test as a pretest.

2.1 Using the Writing Process *SE/TWE pp. 48-51*

Teacher's Name _____ Date _____

Grade _____ Class(es) _____ Date(s)_____ M Tu W Th F

FOCUS
LESSON OVERVIEW
Objective: To apply the five stages of the writing process to different types of writing
Skills: analyzing the writing process; planning before writing
Critical Thinking: relating; comparing and contrasting; defining and clarifying; decision making
Speaking and Listening: asking questions; informal speaking; discussing; evaluating; explaining a process

_____ Bellringer and Grammar Link to the Bellringer, TWE p. 48
_____ Motivating Activity, TWE p. 48

TEACH
Guided Practice
_____ L2, Using the Model, TWE p. 49
_____ L1, Using a Familiar Model, TWE p. 49
_____ Two-Minute Skill Drill, TWE p. 49
_____ Journal Writing Tip, TWE p. 49
_____ L2, Knowing Your Own Process, TWE p. 50
_____ L1, Ordering Steps, TWE p. 50
_____ Enabling Strategies: LEP, TWE p. 50

Independent Practice
_____ *Writing Process Transparencies, 1–10 **
_____ *Fine Art Transparencies, 6–10 **
_____ *Writing Across the Curriculum, p. 4 **
_____ *Cooperative Learning Activities, pp. 7–12 **
_____ *Thinking and Study Skills, pp. 4–5, 9–11 **
_____ *Sentence Combining Practice, p. 1 **
_____ *Speaking and Listening Activities, pp. 12–13 **
_____ *Composition Practice, p. 7 **

ASSESS
_____ Writing Activities Evaluation Guidelines, TWE p. 51
_____ Using the Grammar Link, TWE p. 51

Reteaching
_____ *Composition Reteaching, p. 7 **

Enrichment
_____ *Composition Enrichment, p. 7 **

CLOSE
_____ Close activity, TWE p. 51

* Teacher's Classroom Resources

• Homework Assignments •

_____
_____
_____
_____
_____
_____
_____
_____

Unit Assessment

_____ *Tests with Answer Key*
Unit 2 Choice A Test, p. 5
Unit 2 Choice B Test, p. 6
Unit 2 Composition Objective
Test, pp. 7–8
_____ *Test Generator*
Unit 2 Choice A Test
Unit 2 Choice B Test
Unit 2 Composition Objective
Test
You may wish to administer either the
Unit 2 Choice A Test or the Unit 2
Choice B Test as a pretest.

2.2 Prewriting: Finding and Exploring a Topic

SE/TWE pp. 52–55

Teacher's Name _____ Date _____

Grade _____ Class(es) _____ Date(s)_____ M Tu W Th F

FOCUS
LESSON OVERVIEW
Objective: To use prewriting techniques to generate a topic
Skills: brainstorming and evaluating ideas; planning before writing
Critical Thinking: relating; analyzing; recalling; establishing and evaluating criteria; generating new information; decision making
Speaking and Listening: note taking; asking questions; explaining a process

_____ Bellringer and Grammar Link to the Bellringer, TWE p. 52
_____ Motivating Activity, TWE p. 52

TEACH
Guided Practice
_____ L2, Using Visuals to Generate Writing Ideas, TWE p. 53
_____ L3, Writing About Everyday Experiences, TWE p. 53
_____ Two-Minute Skill Drill, TWE p. 53
_____ Journal Writing Tip, TWE p. 53
_____ L2, Making Clusters, TWE p. 54
_____ Enabling Strategies: LEP, TWE p. 54

Independent Practice
_____ *Fine Art Transparencies, 6–10* *
_____ *Writing Process Transparencies, 1–10* *
_____ *Writing Across the Curriculum, p. 5* *
_____ *Cooperative Learning Activities, pp. 7–12* *
_____ *Thinking and Study Skills, pp. 3-5, 8, 16* *
_____ *Speaking and Listening Activities, pp. 12-13* *
_____ *Composition Practice, p. 8* *

ASSESS
_____ Writing Activities Evaluation Guidelines, TWE p. 55
_____ Using the Grammar Link, TWE p. 55

Reteaching
_____ *Composition Reteaching, p. 8* *

Enrichment
_____ *Composition Enrichment, p. 8* *
_____ *Fine Art Transparencies, 6–10* *
_____ About the Art, TWE p. 55

CLOSE
_____ Close activity, TWE p. 55

* Teacher's Classroom Resources

• Homework Assignments •

_____
_____
_____
_____
_____
_____
_____
_____
_____

2.3 Prewriting: Determining Purpose and Audience *SE/TWE pp. 56–59*

Teacher's Name _____ Date _____

Grade _____ Class(es) _____ Date(s) _____ M Tu W Th F

FOCUS
LESSON OVERVIEW
Objective: To identify the purpose of and audience for a piece of writing
Skills: identifying an audience; determining purpose; planning before writing
Critical Thinking: analyzing; establishing and evaluating criteria; generating new information; making decisions
Speaking and Listening: discussing; evaluating; asking questions

_____ Bellringer and Grammar Link to the Bellringer, TWE p. 56
_____ Motivating Activity, TWE p. 56

TEACH
Guided Practice
_____ L2, Using the Model, TWE p. 57
_____ L1, Using Visual Clues to Determine Purpose, TWE p. 57
_____ Two-Minute Skill Drill, TWE p. 57
_____ Journal Writing Tip, TWE p. 57
_____ L3, Determining the Audience, TWE p. 58
_____ Enabling Strategies: LEP, TWE p. 58

Independent Practice
_____ *Fine Art Transparencies, 6–10 **
_____ *Writing Process Transparencies, 1–10 **
_____ *Writing Across the Curriculum, p. 6 **
_____ *Cooperative Learning Activities, pp. 7–12 **
_____ *Thinking and Study Skills, pp. 3–5, 9, 21 **
_____ *Speaking and Listening Activities, pp. 12-13 **
_____ *Composition Practice, p. 9 **

```
• Homework Assignments •

_____
_____
_____
_____
_____
_____
_____
_____
```

ASSESS
_____ Writing Activities Evaluation Guidelines, TWE p. 59
_____ Using the Grammar Link, TWE p. 59

Reteaching
_____ *Composition Reteaching, p. 9 **

Enrichment
_____ *Composition Enrichment, p. 9 **

CLOSE
_____ Close activity, TWE p. 59

* Teacher's Classroom Resources

2.4 Prewriting: Ordering Ideas *SE/TWE pp. 60–63*

Teacher's Name _____ Date _____

Grade _____ Class(es) _____ Date(s)_____ M Tu W Th F

FOCUS
LESSON OVERVIEW
Objective: To prioritize ideas during prewriting
Skills: putting ideas in logical order; identifying the main idea; choosing supporting details
Critical Thinking: analyzing; identifying the main idea; recalling; establishing and evaluating criteria; decision making
Speaking and Listening: note taking; asking questions; explaining a process

_____ Bellringer and Grammar Link to the Bellringer, TWE p. 60
_____ Motivating Activity, TWE p. 60

TEACH
Guided Practice
_____ L2, Discussing Purpose, TWE p. 61
_____ L1, Identifying Main Ideas, TWE p. 61
_____ Two-Minute Skill Drill, TWE p. 61
_____ Journal Writing Tip, TWE p. 61
_____ L2, Rewriting the Details, TWE p. 62
_____ Two-Minute Skill Drill, TWE p. 62
_____ Enabling Strategies: LEP, TWE p. 62

Independent Practice
_____ *Writing Process Transparencies, 1–10* *
_____ *Fine Art Transparencies, 6–10* *
_____ *Writing Across the Curriculum, p. 7* *
_____ *Cooperative Learning Activities, pp. 7–12* *
_____ *Thinking and Study Skills, pp. 7–8, 11, 13* *
_____ *Speaking and Listening Activities, pp. 7–12* *
_____ *Composition Practice, p. 10* *

ASSESS
_____ Writing Activities Evaluation Guidelines, TWE p. 63
_____ Cross-Curricular: Science, TWE p. 63
_____ Using the Grammar Link, TWE p. 63

Reteaching
_____ *Composition Reteaching, p. 10* *

Enrichment
_____ *Composition Enrichment, p. 10* *
_____ *Fine Art Transparencies, 6–10* *
_____ About the Art, TWE p. 63

CLOSE
_____ Close activity, TWE p. 63

* Teacher's Classroom Resources

• *Homework Assignments* •

_____
_____
_____
_____
_____
_____
_____
_____
_____

2.5 Drafting: Getting It in Writing *SE/TWE pp. 64–67*

Teacher's Name _____ Date _____

Grade _____ Class(es) _____ Date(s)_____ M Tu W Th F

FOCUS
LESSON OVERVIEW
Objective: To generate a first draft from prewriting notes
Skills: using prewriting notes effectively; evaluating peer suggestions; choosing writing techniques to ensure completion
Critical Thinking: analyzing; relating; generating new information; decision making
Speaking and Listening: explaining a process; asking questions; evaluating

_____ Bellringer and Grammar Link to the Bellringer, TWE p. 64
_____ Motivating Activity, TWE p. 64

TEACH
Guided Practice
_____ L2, Promoting Discussion, TWE p. 65
_____ Two-Minute Skill Drill, TWE p. 65
_____ Journal Writing Tip, TWE p. 65
_____ L2, Peer Reviewing Strategies, TWE p. 66
_____ Enabling Strategies: LEP, TWE p. 66

Independent Practice
_____ *Writing Process Transparencies,* 1–10 *
_____ *Fine Art Transparencies,* 6–10 *
_____ *Writing Across the Curriculum,* p. 8 *
_____ *Cooperative Learning Activities,* pp. 7–12 *
_____ *Thinking and Study Skills,* pp. 4–5, 13, 20–22 *
_____ *Speaking and Listening Activities,* pp. 12–13 *
_____ *Composition Practice,* p. 11 *

• Homework Assignments •
_____
_____
_____
_____
_____
_____
_____
_____
_____

ASSESS
_____ Writing Activities Evaluation Guidelines, TWE p. 67
_____ Cross-Curricular: Health and Safety, TWE p. 67
_____ Using the Grammar Link, TWE p. 67

Reteaching
_____ *Composition Reteaching,* p. 11 *

Enrichment
_____ *Composition Enrichment,* p. 11 *
_____ *Fine Art Transparencies,* 6–10 *
_____ About the Art, TWE p. 67

CLOSE
_____ Close activity, TWE p. 67

* Teacher's Classroom Resources

2.6 Revising: Evaluating a Draft *SE/TWE pp. 68–71*

Teacher's Name _____ Date _____

Grade _____ Class(es) _____ Date(s)_____ M Tu W Th F

FOCUS
LESSON OVERVIEW
Objective: To revise a piece of writing for clarity and sense
Skills: scrutinizing and evaluating a draft; giving and receiving a second opinion; evaluating suggestions
Critical Thinking: analyzing; defining and clarifying; decision making
Speaking and Listening: giving and receiving feedback; asking questions; evaluating

_____ Bellringer and Grammar Link to the Bellringer, TWE p. 68
_____ Motivating Activity, TWE p. 68

TEACH
Guided Practice
_____ L2, Using the Model, TWE p. 69
_____ L1, Checking the Writing, TWE p. 69
_____ Two-Minute Skill Drill, TWE p. 69
_____ Journal Writing Tip, TWE p. 69
_____ L2, Understanding the Connections, TWE p. 70
_____ Enabling Strategies: LEP, TWE p. 70

Independent Practice
_____ *Fine Art Transparencies*, 6–10 *
_____ *Writing Process Transparencies*, 1–10 *
_____ *Writing Across the Curriculum*, p. 4 *
_____ *Cooperative Learning Activities*, pp. 7–12 *
_____ *Thinking and Study Skills*, pp. 4, 9, 13, 18 *
_____ *Sentence Combining Practice*, p. 1 *
_____ *Speaking and Listening Activities*, pp. 12–13 *
_____ *Composition Practice*, p. 12 *

ASSESS
_____ Writing Activities Evaluation Guidelines, TWE p. 71
_____ Cross-Curricular: Art, TWE p. 71
_____ Using the Grammar Link, TWE p. 71

Reteaching
_____ *Composition Reteaching*, p. 12 *

Enrichment
_____ *Composition Enrichment*, p. 12 *
_____ *Fine Art Transparencies*, 6–10 *
_____ About the Art, TWE p. 71

CLOSE
_____ Close activity, TWE p. 71

* Teacher's Classroom Resources

```
┌─────────────────────────────────┐
│  • Homework Assignments •        │
│                                  │
│  _____   │
│  _____   │
│  _____   │
│  _____   │
│  _____   │
│  _____   │
│  _____   │
│  _____   │
│  _____   │
└─────────────────────────────────┘
```

2.7 Revising: Making Paragraphs Effective

SE/TWE pp. 72–75

Teacher's Name _____ Date _____
Grade _____ Class(es) _____ Date(s)_____ M Tu W Th F

FOCUS
LESSON OVERVIEW
Objective: To revise a piece of writing for unity and sense
Skills: linking related thoughts in sentences and paragraphs; using effective transitions; identifying the main idea
Critical Thinking: analyzing; activating prior knowledge; synthesizing; making inferences; developing a main idea
Speaking and Listening: giving and receiving feedback; evaluating

_____ Bellringer and Grammar Link to the Bellringer, TWE p. 72
_____ Motivating Activity, TWE p. 72

TEACH
Guided Practice
_____ L2, Using the Model, TWE p. 73
_____ L3, Understanding Creative License, TWE p. 73
_____ Journal Writing Tip, TWE p. 73
_____ L2, Promoting Discussion, TWE p. 74
_____ Two-Minute Skill Drill, TWE p. 74
_____ Enabling Strategies: LEP, TWE p. 74

Independent Practice
_____ *Fine Art Transparencies, 6–10* *
_____ *Writing Process Transparencies, 1–10* *
_____ *Writing Across the Curriculum, p. 8* *
_____ *Cooperative Learning Activities, pp. 7–12* *
_____ *Thinking and Study Skills, pp. 9, 11, 13* *
_____ *Sentence Combining Practice, p. 1* *
_____ *Speaking and Listening Activities, pp. 12–13* *
_____ *Composition Practice, p. 13* *

ASSESS
_____ Writing Activities Evaluation Guidelines, TWE p. 75
_____ Using the Grammar Link, TWE p. 75

Reteaching
_____ *Composition Reteaching, p. 13* *

Enrichment
_____ *Composition Enrichment, p. 13* *

CLOSE
_____ Close activity, TWE p. 75

* Teacher's Classroom Resources

• Homework Assignments •
_____
_____
_____
_____
_____
_____
_____
_____

2.8 Revising: Creating Sentence Variety

SE/TWE pp. 76–79

Teacher's Name _____ Date _____

Grade _____ Class(es) _____ Date(s)_____ M Tu W Th F

FOCUS
LESSON OVERVIEW
Objective: To revise a piece of writing by combining sentences and by varying sentence length and word order

Skills: expressing relationships between thoughts; combining similar thoughts; varying word order to create rhythm in writing

Critical Thinking: analyzing; identifying the main idea; comparing and contrasting; decision making; patterning

Speaking and Listening: evaluating; interpreting clues; discussing; giving and receiving feedback

_____ Bellringer and Grammar Link to the Bellringer, TWE p. 76
_____ Motivating Activity, TWE p. 76

TEACH
Guided Practice
_____ L2, Reviewing Sentences, TWE p. 77
_____ L2, Connecting Ideas, TWE p. 77
_____ Journal Writing Tip, TWE p. 77
_____ L2, Revising with a Partner, TWE p. 78
_____ Two-Minute Skill Drill, TWE p. 78
_____ Enabling Strategies: LEP, TWE p. 78

Independent Practice
_____ *Fine Art Transparencies, 6–10* *
_____ *Writing Process Transparencies, 1–10* *
_____ *Writing Across the Curriculum, p. 7* *
_____ *Cooperative Learning Activities, pp. 7–12* *
_____ *Thinking and Study Skills, pp. 1, 4, 20* *
_____ *Sentence Combining Practice, p. 1* *
_____ *Speaking and Listening Activities, pp. 12–13* *
_____ *Composition Practice, p. 14* *

ASSESS
_____ Writing Activities Evaluation Guidelines, TWE p. 79
_____ Cross-Curricular: Art, TWE p. 79
_____ Using the Grammar Link, TWE p. 79

Reteaching
_____ *Composition Reteaching, p. 14* *

Enrichment
_____ *Composition Enrichment, p. 14* *
_____ *Fine Art Transparencies, 6–10* *
_____ About the Art, TWE p. 79

• Homework Assignments •

_____
_____
_____
_____
_____
_____
_____

CLOSE
_____ Close activity, TWE p. 79

* Teacher's Classroom Resources

2.9 Editing: Making Final Adjustments

SE/TWE pp. 80–83

Teacher's Name _____ Date _____

Grade _____ Class(es) _____ Date(s)_____ M Tu W Th F

FOCUS
LESSON OVERVIEW
Objective: To edit a piece of writing for grammar, usage, and mechanics and to proofread using standard proofreading symbols
Skills: proofreading; editing for grammar, usage, and mechanics; using proofreading symbols
Critical Thinking: analyzing; evaluating; decision making
Speaking and Listening: discussing; giving and receiving feedback

_____ Bellringer and Grammar Link to the Bellringer, TWE p. 80
_____ Motivating Activity, TWE p. 80

TEACH
Guided Practice
_____ L2, Discussing Peer-Reviewing Strategies, TWE p. 81
_____ L1, Using the Checklist, TWE p. 81
_____ Journal Writing Tip, TWE p. 81
_____ L2, Using the Model, TWE p. 82
_____ L3, Learning Additional Proofreading Symbols, TWE p. 82
_____ Two-Minute Skill Drill, TWE p. 82
_____ Enabling Strategies: LEP, TWE p. 82

Independent Practice
_____ *Fine Art Transparencies, 6–10 **
_____ *Writing Process Transparencies, 1–10 **
_____ *Writing Across the Curriculum, p. 10 **
_____ *Cooperative Learning Activities, pp. 7–12 **
_____ *Thinking and Study Skills, pp. 1, 14, 20 **
_____ *Sentence Combining Practice, p. 1 **
_____ *Speaking and Listening Activities, pp. 12–13 **

ASSESS
_____ Writing Activities Evaluation Guidelines, TWE p. 83
_____ Using the Grammar Link, TWE p. 83

Reteaching
_____ *Composition Reteaching, p. 15 **

Enrichment
_____ *Composition Enrichment, p. 15 **

CLOSE
_____ Close activity, TWE p. 83

* Teacher's Classroom Resources

• Homework Assignments •

_____
_____
_____
_____
_____
_____
_____
_____

2.10 Presenting: Sharing Your Writing

SE/TWE pp. 84–87

Teacher's Name _____ Date _____

Grade _____ Class(es) _____ Date(s)_____ M Tu W Th F

FOCUS

LESSON OVERVIEW

Objective: To select a format and publish a piece of writing

Skills: presenting; writing; evaluating different formats for an intended audience; comparing forms of publication

Critical Thinking: analyzing; comparing and contrasting; decision making; visualizing; inferring; categorizing

Speaking and Listening: giving and receiving feedback; formal speaking; oral reports

_____ Bellringer and Grammar Link to the Bellringer, TWE p. 84
_____ Motivating Activity, TWE p. 84

TEACH

Guided Practice

_____ L2, Preparing an Oral Presentation, TWE p. 85
_____ Journal Writing Tip, TWE p. 85
_____ L3, Using a Thesaurus, TWE p. 86
_____ Two-Minute Skill Drill, TWE p. 86
_____ Enabling Strategies: LEP, TWE p. 86

Independent Practice

_____ *Fine Art Transparencies, 6–10* *
_____ *Writing Process Transparencies, 1–10* *
_____ *Writing Across the Curriculum, p. 21* *
_____ *Cooperative Learning Activities, pp. 7–12* *
_____ *Thinking and Study Skills, pp. 6, 13, 20–22* *
_____ *Speaking and Listening Activities, pp. 12–13* *
_____ *Composition Practice, p. 16* *

ASSESS

_____ Writing Activities Evaluation Guidelines, TWE p. 87
_____ Using the Grammar Link, TWE p. 87

Reteaching

_____ *Composition Reteaching, p. 16* *

Enrichment

_____ *Composition Enrichment, p. 16* *

CLOSE

_____ Close activity, TWE p. 87

* Teacher's Classroom Resources

• Homework Assignments •

_____
_____
_____
_____
_____
_____
_____
_____
_____

Unit 2 Writing Process in Action *SE/TWE pp. 88–91*

Teacher's Name _____ Date _____

Grade _____ Class(es) _____ Date(s)_____ M Tu W Th F

FOCUS
LESSON OVERVIEW
Objective: To use the writing process to write a brief profile of a courageous person
Skills: using the five stages of the writing process: prewriting, drafting, revising, editing, and presenting
Critical Thinking: identifying the main idea; decision making; summarizing; building background
Speaking and Listening: informal speaking; interviewing; discussing

_____ Bellringer and Grammar Link to the Bellringer, TWE p. 88
_____ Motivating Activity, TWE p. 88

TEACH
Prewriting
_____ L2, Developing Ideas for Writing, TWE p. 89
_____ *Thinking and Study Skills*, pp. 4–6, 9, 13, 17, 22 *

Drafting
_____ L1, Beginning the Profile, TWE p. 89

Revising
_____ L2, Peer Editing, TWE p. 90

Editing
_____ L2, Peer Editing, TWE p. 90

Presenting
_____ Presenting activity, TWE p. 90

_____ Journal Writing Tip, TWE p. 90
_____ Enrichment and Extension, TWE p. 90
_____ Enabling Strategies: LEP, TWE p. 91

Independent Practice
_____ *Writing Process Transparencies*, 1–10 *
_____ *Thinking and Study Skills*, pp. 4–6, 9, 13, 17, 22 *
_____ *Sentence Combining Practice*, p. 1 *
_____ *Composition Practice*, p. 17 *
_____ **Grammar Workbook**, Lessons 69–71

ASSESS
_____ Evaluation Guidelines, TWE p. 91

Reteaching
_____ *Composition Reteaching*, p. 17 *

Enrichment
_____ *Composition Enrichment*, p. 17 *

CLOSE
_____ Close activity, TWE p. 91

* Teacher's Classroom Resources

• Homework Assignments •

_____
_____
_____
_____
_____
_____
_____
_____

Unit 2 Literature: from *The Clay Marble*, Minfong Ho *SE/TWE pp. 92–97*

Teacher's Name _____ Date _____

Grade _____ Class(es) _____ Date(s)_____ M Tu W Th F

FOCUS
LESSON OVERVIEW
Objective: To read a passage and understand narrative fiction
Skills: reading comprehension
Critical Thinking: synthesizing; recalling; inferring; visualizing
Speaking and Listening: discussing

_____ Bellringer and Motivating Activity, TWE pp. 92–93

TEACH
Guided Practice
_____ L2, Guided Reading, TWE pp. 93–96
_____ About the Art, TWE p. 94
_____ Genre and Style, TWE p. 94
_____ Writers and Writing, TWE p. 95
_____ Cultural Diversity, TWE p. 95
_____ About the Art, TWE p. 96
_____ Connections Across the Curriculum: History, TWE p. 97

Independent Practice
_____ *Fine Art Transparencies*, 6–10 *
_____ *Speaking and Listening Activities*, pp. 6–8 *
_____ *Thinking and Study Skills*, pp. 3–5, 9, 33, 34 *

ASSESS
_____ Evaluation Guidelines for Discussion, TWE p. 97

CLOSE
_____ Close activity, TWE p. 97

* Teacher's Classroom Resources

• *Homework Assignments* •

_____
_____
_____
_____
_____
_____
_____
_____
_____

UNIT 2 REVIEW *p. 98*
_____ Reflecting on the Unit, TWE p. 98
_____ Writing Across the Curriculum, TWE p. 98
_____ Adding to Your Portfolio, TWE p. 98
_____ Portfolio Evaluation Guidelines, TWE p. 98

Unit Assessment
_____ *Tests with Answer Key*
Unit 2 Choice A Test, p. 5
Unit 2 Choice B Test, p. 6
Unit 2 Composition Objective
Test, pp. 7–8
_____ *Test Generator*
Unit 2 Choice A Test
Unit 2 Choice B Test
Unit 2 Composition Objective
Test
You may wish to administer one of these tests as a mastery test.

Unit 3 Case Study: Descriptive Writing *SE/TWE pp. 100–105*

Teacher's Name _____ Date _____

Grade _____ Class(es) _____ Date(s)_____ M Tu W Th F

FOCUS

LESSON OVERVIEW

Objective: To develop descriptions that achieve specific goals
Skills: defining a purpose; choosing words for their connotations
Critical Thinking: defining and clarifying; visualizing; making inferences
Speaking and Listening: questioning; evaluating; discussing; explaining a process

_____ Bellringer and Grammar Link to the Bellringer, TWE p. 100
_____ Motivating Activity, TWE p. 100

TEACH

_____ Building Background, TWE p. 101
_____ Preview the Case Study, TWE p. 101
_____ Discussion Prompts, TWE pp. 102, 103
_____ Cultural Diversity, TWE p. 102
_____ Connections Across the Curriculum: History, TWE p. 103
_____ Civil Literacy, TWE p. 104

Guided Practice

_____ L2, Discussion, TWE p. 104

Independent Practice

_____ *Writing Process Transparencies, 11–13B* *
_____ *Cooperative Learning Activities, pp. 13–18* *
_____ *Case Studies: Writing in the Real World, pp. 9–12* *
_____ *Thinking and Study Skills, pp. 3, 5, 9, 22* *

ASSESS

_____ Responding to the Case Study, TWE p. 105
_____ Using the Grammar Link, TWE p. 105

Reteaching

_____ Reteaching activity, TWE p. 105

Enrichment

_____ Enrichment activity, TWE p. 105

CLOSE

_____ Close activity, TWE p. 105

* Teacher's Classroom Resources

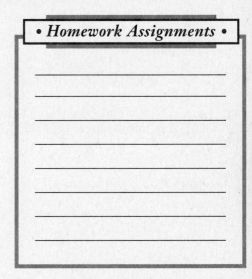

• Homework Assignments •

_____
_____
_____
_____
_____
_____
_____
_____

Unit Assessment

_____ *Tests with Answer Key*
Unit 3 Choice A Test, p. 9
Unit 3 Choice B Test, p. 10
Unit 3 Composition Objective
Test, pp. 11–12
_____ *Test Generator*
Unit 3 Choice A Test
Unit 3 Choice B Test
Unit 3 Composition Objective
Test
You may wish to administer either the
Unit 3 Choice A Test or the Unit 3
Choice B Test as a pretest.

3.1 Writing to Show, Not Tell *SE/TWE pp. 106–109*

Teacher's Name _____ Date _____

Grade _____ Class(es) _____ Date(s)_____ M Tu W Th F

FOCUS
LESSON OVERVIEW
Objective: To describe people, places, and things using vivid sensory details
Skills: choosing words for their sensory appeal; contrasting writing that shows and writing that tells
Critical Thinking: comparing and contrasting; visualizing; analyzing; decision making
Speaking and Listening: informal speaking; discussing; evaluating; explaining a process

_____ Bellringer and Grammar Link to the Bellringer, TWE p. 106
_____ Motivating Activity, TWE p. 106

TEACH
Guided Practice
_____ L2, Using the Model, TWE p. 107
_____ L1, Categorizing Details, TWE p. 107
_____ Two-Minute Skill Drill, TWE p. 107
_____ Journal Writing Tip, TWE p. 107
_____ L2, Promoting Discussion, TWE p. 108
_____ Enabling Strategies: LEP, TWE p. 108

Independent Practice
_____ *Fine Art Transparencies*, 11–14 *
_____ *Writing Process Transparencies*, 11–13B *
_____ *Writing Across the Curriculum*, p. 20 *
_____ *Cooperative Learning Activities*, pp. 13–18 *
_____ *Thinking and Study Skills*, pp. 3, 9, 12 *
_____ *Sentence Combining Practice*, p. 24 *
_____ *Speaking and Listening Activities*, pp. 14–15 *
_____ *Composition Practice*, p. 18 *

ASSESS
_____ Writing Activities Evaluation Guidelines, TWE p. 109
_____ Cross-Curricular: Art, TWE p. 109
_____ Using the Grammar Link, TWE p. 109

Reteaching
_____ *Composition Reteaching*, p. 18 *

Enrichment
_____ *Composition Enrichment*, p. 18 *
_____ *Fine Art Transparencies*, 11–14 *
_____ About the Art, TWE p. 109

CLOSE
_____ Close activity, TWE p. 109

* Teacher's Classroom Resources

• Homework Assignments •

_____
_____
_____
_____
_____
_____
_____
_____

Unit Assessment
_____ *Tests with Answer Key*
Unit 3 Choice A Test, p. 9
Unit 3 Choice B Test, p. 10
Unit 3 Composition Objective
    Test, pp. 11–12
_____ *Test Generator*
Unit 3 Choice A Test
Unit 3 Choice B Test
Unit 3 Composition Objective
    Test
You may wish to administer either the
Unit 3 Choice A Test or the Unit 3
Choice B Test as a pretest.

3.2 Combining Observation and Imagination

SE/TWE pp. 110–113

Teacher's Name _____ Date _____

Grade _____ Class(es) _____ Date(s)_____ M Tu W Th F

FOCUS

LESSON OVERVIEW

Objective: To recall sensory details from experience and to synthesize them into vivid descriptions

Skills: choosing words for sensory appeal; using sensory language to attract and retain a reader's attention

Critical Thinking: visualizing; activating prior knowledge; generating new information; decision making

Speaking and Listening: informal speaking; discussing; explaining a process

_____ Bellringer and Grammar Link to the Bellringer, TWE p. 110
_____ Motivating Activity, TWE p. 110

TEACH

Guided Practice

_____ L2, Using the Model, TWE p. 111
_____ L3, Teaching from the Art, TWE p. 111
_____ About the Art, TWE p. 111
_____ Two-Minute Skill Drill, TWE p. 111
_____ Journal Writing Tip, TWE p. 111
_____ L2, Using the Model, TWE p. 112
_____ Enabling Strategies: LEP, TWE p. 112

Independent Practice

_____ *Fine Art Transparencies*, 11–14 *
_____ *Writing Process Transparencies*, 11–13B *
_____ *Writing Across the Curriculum*, p. 20 *
_____ *Cooperative Learning Activities*, pp. 13–18 *
_____ *Thinking and Study Skills*, pp. 3, 9, 12 *
_____ *Speaking and Listening Activities*, pp. 14–15 *
_____ *Sentence Combining Practice*, p. 24 *
_____ *Composition Practice*, p. 19 *

ASSESS

_____ Writing Activities Evaluation Guidelines, TWE p. 113
_____ Using the Grammar Link, TWE p. 113

Reteaching

_____ *Composition Reteaching*, p. 19 *

Enrichment

_____ *Composition Enrichment*, p. 19 *

CLOSE

_____ Close activity, TWE p. 113

* Teacher's Classroom Resources

• Homework Assignments •

_____
_____
_____
_____
_____
_____
_____
_____

3.3 Choosing Details to Create a Mood

SE/TWE pp. 114–117

Teacher's Name _____ Date _____

Grade _____ Class(es) _____ Date(s)_____ M Tu W Th F

FOCUS
LESSON OVERVIEW
Objective: To create a mood in descriptive writing through the use of appropriate details
Skills: choosing words to create a mood; analyzing words to determine the mood they create
Critical Thinking: visualizing; activating prior knowledge; comparing and contrasting; recalling; relating; decision making
Speaking and Listening: informal speaking; discussing; explaining a process

_____ Bellringer and Grammar Link to the Bellringer, TWE p. 114
_____ Motivating Activity, TWE p. 114

TEACH
Guided Practice
_____ L2, Using the Model, TWE p. 115
_____ L2, Analyzing Emotions, TWE p. 115
_____ Two-Minute Skill Drill, TWE p. 115
_____ Journal Writing Tip, TWE p. 115
_____ L2, Using the Model, TWE p. 116
_____ L3, Promoting Discussion, TWE p. 116
_____ Enabling Strategies: LEP, TWE p. 116

Independent Practice
_____ *Fine Art Transparencies, 11–14 **
_____ *Writing Process Transparencies, 11–13B **
_____ *Writing Across the Curriculum, p. 20 **
_____ *Cooperative Learning Activities, pp. 13–18 **
_____ *Thinking and Study Skills, pp. 3–5, 9 **
_____ *Speaking and Listening Activities, pp. 14–15 **
_____ *Composition Practice, p. 20 **
_____ *Sentence Combining Practice, p. 24 **

ASSESS
_____ Writing Activities Evaluation Guidelines, TWE p. 117
_____ Using the Grammar Link, TWE p. 117

Reteaching
_____ *Composition Reteaching, p. 20 **

Enrichment
_____ *Composition Enrichment, p. 20 **

CLOSE
_____ Close activity, TWE p. 117

* Teacher's Classroom Resources

• *Homework Assignments* •
_____
_____
_____
_____
_____
_____
_____
_____
_____

3.4 Organizing Details in a Description

SE/TWE pp. 118–121

Teacher's Name _____ Date _____

Grade _____ Class(es) _____ Date(s)_____ M Tu W Th F

FOCUS
LESSON OVERVIEW
Objective: To present details in spatial order when describing a scene
Skills: ordering spatial details; choosing transition words and phrases to clarify descriptions
Critical Thinking: recalling; relating; visualizing; activating prior knowledge; comparing and contrasting; evaluating
Speaking and Listening: informal speaking; discussing

_____ Bellringer and Grammar Link to the Bellringer, TWE p. 118
_____ Motivating Activity, TWE p. 118

TEACH
Guided Practice

_____ L2, Using the Model, TWE p. 119
_____ L1, Organizing Tips, TWE p. 119
_____ Two-Minute Skill Drill, TWE p. 119
_____ Journal Writing Tip, TWE p. 119
_____ L2, Using the Model, TWE p. 120
_____ L3, Heightening Descriptions, TWE p. 120
_____ Enabling Strategies: LEP, TWE p. 120

Independent Practice

_____ *Fine Art Transparencies*, 11–14 *
_____ *Writing Process Transparencies*, 11–13B *
_____ *Writing Across the Curriculum*, p. 20 *
_____ *Cooperative Learning Activities*, pp. 13–18 *
_____ *Thinking and Study Skills*, pp. 3–5, 9, 21–22 *
_____ *Sentence Combining Practice*, p. 24 *
_____ *Speaking and Listening Activities*, pp. 14–15 *
_____ *Composition Practice*, p. 21 *

> • **Homework Assignments** •
> _____
> _____
> _____
> _____
> _____
> _____
> _____
> _____

ASSESS

_____ Writing Activities Evaluation Guidelines, TWE p. 121
_____ Cross-Curricular: Mathematics, TWE p. 121
_____ Using the Grammar Link, TWE p. 121

Reteaching
_____ *Composition Reteaching*, p. 21 *

Enrichment
_____ *Composition Enrichment*, p. 21 *
_____ *Fine Art Transparencies*, 11–14 *
_____ About the Art, TWE p. 121

CLOSE
_____ Close activity, TWE p. 121

* Teacher's Classroom Resources

3.5 Describing a Person *SE/TWE pp. 122–125*

Teacher's Name _____ Date _____

Grade _____ Class(es) _____ Date(s)_____ M Tu W Th F

FOCUS
LESSON OVERVIEW
Objective: To communicate the essence of a character by describing the individual's appearance and behavior
Skills: analyzing techniques used to create memorable characters; selecting and arranging details to create memorable characters
Critical Thinking: recalling; relating; visualizing; inferring; analyzing
Speaking and Listening: informal speaking; discussing

_____ Bellringer and Grammar Link to the Bellringer, TWE p. 122
_____ Motivating Activity, TWE p. 122

TEACH
Guided Practice
_____ L2, Using the Model, TWE p. 123
_____ L2, Identifying by Description, TWE p. 123
_____ Two-Minute Skill Drill, TWE p. 123
_____ Journal Writing Tip, TWE p. 123
_____ L2, Using the Model, TWE p. 124
_____ L3, Promoting Discussion, TWE p. 124
_____ Enabling Strategies: LEP, TWE p. 124

Independent Practice
_____ *Fine Art Transparencies*, 11–14 *
_____ *Writing Process Transparencies*, 11–13B *
_____ *Writing Across the Curriculum*, p. 20 *
_____ *Cooperative Learning Activities*, pp. 13–18 *
_____ *Thinking and Study Skills*, pp. 3–5, 9, 12, 17 *
_____ *Speaking and Listening Activities*, pp. 14–15 *
_____ *Sentence Combining Practice*, p. 24 *
_____ *Composition Practice*, p. 22 *

ASSESS
_____ Writing Activities Evaluation Guidelines, TWE p. 125
_____ Using the Grammar Link, TWE p. 125

Reteaching
_____ *Composition Reteaching*, p. 22 *

Enrichment
_____ *Composition Enrichment*, p. 22 *
_____ *Fine Art Transparencies*, 11–14 *
_____ About the Art, TWE p. 125

CLOSE
_____ Close activity, TWE p. 125

* Teacher's Classroom Resources

• Homework Assignments •

_____
_____
_____
_____
_____
_____
_____
_____
_____

3.6 Relating a Poem to Your Experience

SE/TWE pp. 126–129

Teacher's Name _____ Date _____

Grade _____ Class(es) _____ Date(s)_____ M Tu W Th F

FOCUS

LESSON OVERVIEW

Objective: To use sensory images to describe familiar experiences

Skills: relating poetry and experience; creating sensory images for a poem

Critical Thinking: recalling; relating; visualizing; categorizing; analyzing

Speaking and Listening: asking questions; informal speaking; discussing

_____ Bellringer and Grammar Link to the Bellringer, TWE p. 126

_____ Motivating Activity, TWE p. 126

TEACH

Guided Practice

_____ L2, Using the Model, TWE p. 127

_____ L2, Thinking Visually, TWE p. 127

_____ Two-Minute Skill Drill, TWE p. 127

_____ Journal Writing Tip, TWE p. 127

_____ L2, Reacting to Poetry, TWE p. 128

_____ L1, Building Writing Confidence, TWE p. 128

_____ Enabling Strategies: LEP, TWE p. 128

Independent Practice

_____ *Fine Art Transparencies, 11–14 ***

_____ *Writing Process Transparencies, 11–13B ***

_____ *Writing Across the Curriculum, p. 20 ***

_____ *Cooperative Learning Activities, pp. 13–18 ***

_____ *Thinking and Study Skills, pp. 3–6, 8, 12, 22 ***

_____ *Sentence Combining Practice, p. 24 ***

_____ *Speaking and Listening Activities, pp. 14–15 ***

_____ *Composition Practice, p. 23 ***

• Homework Assignments •

_____

_____

_____

_____

_____

_____

_____

_____

ASSESS

_____ Writing Activities Evaluation Guidelines, TWE p. 129

_____ Using the Grammar Link, TWE p. 129

Reteaching

_____ *Composition Reteaching, p. 23 ***

Enrichment

_____ *Composition Enrichment, p. 23 ***

CLOSE

_____ Close activity, TWE p. 129

* Teacher's Classroom Resources

Unit 3 Writing Process in Action *SE/TWE pp. 130–133*

Teacher's Name _____ Date _____
Grade _____ Class(es) _____ Date(s)_____ M Tu W Th F

FOCUS
LESSON OVERVIEW
Objective: To develop a travel article for teens, using vivid details to create an appealing description
Skills: using the five stages of the writing process: prewriting, drafting, revising, editing, and presenting; using descriptive words; writing for a specific audience and purpose
Critical Thinking: analyzing; synthesizing; visualizing; defining and clarifying
Speaking and Listening: formal speaking; informal speaking

_____ Bellringer and Grammar Link to the Bellringer, TWE p. 130
_____ Motivating Activity, TWE p. 130

TEACH
Prewriting
_____ L2, Developing Ideas for Descriptive Writing, TWE p. 131
_____ *Thinking and Study Skills*, pp. 3, 8, 9 *

Drafting
_____ L3, Including Cultural Information, TWE p. 131

Revising
_____ L2, Peer Editing, TWE p. 132

Editing
_____ L2, Peer Editing, TWE p. 132

Presenting
_____ Presenting activity, TWE p. 132

_____ Journal Writing Tip, TWE p. 132
_____ Enrichment and Extension, TWE p. 132
_____ Beyond the Classroom, TWE p. 133

Independent Practice
_____ *Writing Process Transparencies*, 11–13B *
_____ *Thinking and Study Skills*, pp. 3, 8, 9 *
_____ *Sentence Combining Practice*, p. 24 *
_____ *Composition Practice*, p. 24 *
_____ **Grammar Workbook**, Lesson 93

ASSESS
_____ Evaluation Guidelines, TWE p. 133

Reteaching
_____ *Composition Reteaching*, p. 24 *

Enrichment
_____ *Composition Enrichment*, p. 24 *

• Homework Assignments •

_____
_____
_____
_____
_____
_____
_____
_____

CLOSE
_____ Close activity, TWE p. 133

* Teacher's Classroom Resources

Unit 3 Literature: from *The Gathering*, Virginia Hamilton *SE/TWE pp. 134–139*

Teacher's Name _____ Date _____

Grade _____ Class(es) _____ Date(s)_____ M Tu W Th F

FOCUS

LESSON OVERVIEW

Objective: To examine how a well-known children's writer uses detailed descriptions to convey an imaginary world

Skills: reading comprehension

Critical Thinking: visualizing; comparing; summarizing

Speaking and Listening: discussing

_____ Bellringer and Motivating Activity, TWE p. 134

TEACH

Guided Practice

_____ L2, Guided Reading, TWE pp. 135–138

_____ About the Art, TWE p. 135

_____ About the Art, TWE p. 136

_____ Genre and Style, TWE p. 136

_____ Writers and Writing, TWE p. 137

_____ Technology Tip, TWE p. 138

_____ Enrichment and Extension, TWE p. 139

Independent Practice

_____ *Fine Art Transparencies*, 11–15 *

_____ *Thinking and Study Skills*, pp. 3, 5, 22 *

_____ *Speaking and Listening Activities*, pp. 17–18 *

ASSESS

_____ Evaluation Guidelines for Discussion, TWE p. 139

CLOSE

_____ Close activity, TWE p. 139

* Teacher's Classroom Resources

• Homework Assignments •

_____

_____

_____

_____

_____

_____

_____

_____

_____

_____

UNIT 3 REVIEW *p. 140*

_____ Reflecting on the Unit, TWE p. 140

_____ Writing Across the Curriculum, TWE p. 140

_____ Adding to Your Portfolio, TWE p. 140

_____ Portfolio Evaluation, TWE p. 140

Unit Assessment

_____ *Tests with Answer Key*

Unit 3 Choice A Test, p. 9

Unit 3 Choice B Test, p. 10

Unit 3 Composition Objective Test, pp. 11–12

_____ *Test Generator*

Unit 3 Choice A Test

Unit 3 Choice B Test

Unit 3 Composition Objective Test

You may wish to administer one of these tests as a mastery test.

Unit 4 Case Study: Narrative Writing *SE/TWE pp. 142–147*

Teacher's Name _____ Date _____

Grade _____ Class(es) _____ Date(s)_____ M Tu W Th F

FOCUS
LESSON OVERVIEW
Objective: To understand the elements required for successful narrative writing
Skills: analyzing; writing a short narrative
Critical Thinking: relating a specific example to a general model; building background
Speaking and Listening: discussing

_____ Bellringer and Grammar Link to the Bellringer, TWE p. 142
_____ Motivating Activity, TWE p. 142

TEACH
_____ Building Background, TWE p. 143
_____ Preview the Case Study, TWE p. 143
_____ Discussion Prompts, TWE pp. 144, 145
_____ Cultural Diversity, TWE p. 144
_____ Connections Across the Curriculum: Government, TWE p. 145
_____ Cooperative Learning, TWE p. 146

Guided Practice
_____ L2, Discussion, TWE p. 146

Independent Practice
_____ *Writing Process Transparencies*, 14–16B *
_____ *Cooperative Learning Activities*, pp. 19–24 *
_____ *Case Studies: Writing in the Real World*, pp. 13–16 *
_____ *Thinking and Study Skills*, pp. 5, 18, 22 *

ASSESS
_____ Responding to the Case Study, TWE p. 147
_____ Using the Grammar Link, TWE p. 147

Reteaching
_____ Reteaching activity, TWE p. 147

Enrichment
_____ Enrichment activity, TWE p. 147

CLOSE
_____ Close activity, TWE p. 147

* Teacher's Classroom Resources

• *Homework Assignments* •

_____
_____
_____
_____
_____
_____
_____
_____
_____

Unit Assessment

_____ *Tests with Answer Key*
Unit 4 Choice A Test, p. 13
Unit 4 Choice B Test, p. 14
Unit 4 Composition Objective
Test, pp. 15–16
_____ *Test Generator*
Unit 4 Choice A Test
Unit 4 Choice B Test
Unit 4 Composition Objective
Test
You may wish to administer either the
Unit 4 Choice A Test or the Unit 4
Choice B Test as a pretest.

4.1 Telling a Good Story *SE/TWE pp. 148–151*

Teacher's Name _____ Date _____

Grade _____ Class(es) _____ Date(s)_____ M Tu W Th F

FOCUS
LESSON OVERVIEW
Objective: To generate a story that incorporates characters, setting, and plot

Skills: analyzing literary models; planning before writing; identifying the attributes and components of a story

Critical Thinking: relating; decision-making patterns; activating prior knowledge; generating new information

Speaking and Listening: note taking; asking questions; informal speaking; discussing; evaluating; explaining a process

_____ Bellringer and Grammar Link to the Bellringer, TWE p. 148
_____ Motivating Activity, TWE p. 148

TEACH
Guided Practice
_____ L2, Using the Model, TWE p. 149
_____ L2, Promoting Discussion, TWE p. 149
_____ Two-Minute Skill Drill, TWE p. 149
_____ Journal Writing Tip, TWE p. 149
_____ L2, Formulating Questions, TWE p. 150
_____ L1, Choosing Settings, TWE p. 150
_____ Enabling Strategies: LEP, TWE p. 150

Independent Practice
_____ *Fine Art Transparencies, 16–20 ***
_____ *Writing Process Transparencies, 14–16B ***
_____ *Writing Across the Curriculum, p. 19 ***
_____ *Cooperative Learning Activities, pp. 19–24 ***
_____ *Thinking and Study Skills, pp. 4, 22 ***
_____ *Speaking and Listening Activities, p. 23 ***
_____ *Composition Practice, p. 25 ***

ASSESS
_____ Writing Activities Evaluation Guidelines, TWE p. 151
_____ Using the Grammar Link, TWE p. 151

Reteaching
_____ *Composition Reteaching, p. 25 ***

Enrichment
_____ *Composition Enrichment, p. 25 ***

CLOSE
_____ Close activity, TWE p. 151

* Teacher's Classroom Resources

• Homework Assignments •

_____
_____
_____
_____
_____
_____
_____
_____

Unit Assessment

_____ *Tests with Answer Key*
Unit 4 Choice A Test, p. 13
Unit 4 Choice B Test, p. 14
Unit 4 Composition Objective
Test, pp. 15–16
_____ *Test Generator*
Unit 4 Choice A Test
Unit 4 Choice B Test
Unit 4 Composition Objective
Test

You may wish to administer either the Unit 4 Choice A Test or the Unit 4 Choice B Test as a pretest.

4.2 Exploring Story Ideas *SE/TWE pp. 152–155*

Teacher's Name _____ Date _____

Grade _____ Class(es) _____ Date(s)_____ M Tu W Th F

FOCUS

LESSON OVERVIEW

Objective: To explore possible story ideas

Skills: brainstorming, organizing, and developing story ideas; analyzing the components of a story

Critical Thinking: decision making; generating new information; identifying main ideas; analyzing; summarizing; comparing

Speaking and Listening: asking questions; discussing; evaluating; explaining a process

_____ Bellringer and Grammar Link to the Bellringer, TWE p. 152

_____ Motivating Activity, TWE p. 152

TEACH

Guided Practice

_____ L2, Identifying Story Ideas, TWE p. 153

_____ L3, Understanding Types of Conflict, TWE p. 153

_____ Journal Writing Tip, TWE p. 153

_____ L2, Using the Model, TWE p. 154

_____ Two-Minute Skill Drill, TWE p. 154

_____ Enabling Strategies: LEP, TWE p. 154

Independent Practice

_____ *Fine Art Transparencies, 16–21 **

_____ *Writing Process Transparencies, 14–16B **

_____ *Writing Across the Curriculum, p. 6 **

_____ *Cooperative Learning Activities, pp. 19–23 **

_____ *Thinking and Study Skills, pp. 1, 10 **

_____ *Sentence Combining Practice, p. 25 **

_____ *Speaking and Listening Activities, p. 23 **

_____ *Composition Practice, p. 26 **

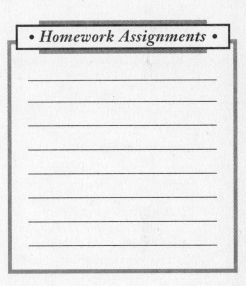

• *Homework Assignments* •

_____

_____

_____

_____

_____

_____

_____

_____

ASSESS

_____ Writing Activities Evaluation Guidelines, TWE p. 155

_____ Computer Option, TWE p. 155

_____ Using the Grammar Link, TWE p. 155

Reteaching

_____ *Composition Reteaching, p. 26 **

Enrichment

_____ *Composition Enrichment, p. 26 **

_____ *Fine Art Transparencies, 16–20 **

_____ About the Art, TWE p. 155

CLOSE

_____ Close activity, TWE p. 155

* Teacher's Classroom Resources

4.3 Using Time Order in a Story *SE/TWE pp.156–159*

Teacher's Name _____ Date _____

Grade _____ Class(es) _____ Date(s)_____ M Tu W Th F

FOCUS
LESSON OVERVIEW
Objective: To express relationships among narrative events, using time order and transition words
Skills: ordering events in time; choosing words to signify transitions
Critical Thinking: analyzing; relating events to one another; synthesizing; recalling; visualizing
Speaking and Listening: note taking; asking questions; discussing; evaluating; explaining a process

_____ Bellringer and Grammar Link to the Bellringer, TWE p. 156
_____ Motivating Activity, TWE p. 156

TEACH
Guided Practice
_____ L2, Using the Model, TWE p. 157
_____ L1, Examining the Model, TWE p. 157
_____ Journal Writing Tip, TWE p.157
_____ L2, Using the Model, TWE p. 158
_____ Two-Minute Skill Drill, TWE p. 158
_____ Enabling Strategies: LEP, TWE p. 158

Independent Practice
_____ *Fine Art Transparencies*, 16–20 *
_____ *Writing Process Transparencies*, 14–16B *
_____ *Writing Across the Curriculum*, p. 7 *
_____ *Cooperative Learning Activities*, pp. 19–24 *
_____ *Thinking and Study Skills*, p. 8 *
_____ *Speaking and Listening Activities*, p. 23 *
_____ *Composition Practice*, p. 27 *
_____ *Sentence Combining Practice*, p. 25 *

ASSESS
_____ Writing Activities Evaluation Guidelines, TWE p. 159
_____ Cross-Curricular: Science, TWE p. 159
_____ Using the Grammar Link, TWE p. 159

Reteaching
_____ *Composition Reteaching*, p. 27 *

Enrichment
_____ *Composition Enrichment*, p. 27 *
_____ *Fine Art Transparencies*, 16–20 *
_____ About the Art, TWE p.159

CLOSE
_____ Close activity, TWE p. 159

* Teacher's Classroom Resources

> ### • *Homework Assignments* •
>
> _____
> _____
> _____
> _____
> _____
> _____
> _____
> _____
> _____

4.4 Writing Dialogue to Develop Characters

SE/TWE pp. 160–163

Teacher's Name _____ Date _____

Grade _____ Class(es) _____ Date(s)_____ M Tu W Th F

FOCUS

LESSON OVERVIEW

Objective: To create dialogue that reveals the personality of one or more believable characters

Skills: choosing words to reveal character; evaluating dialogue on the basis of sound

Critical Thinking: visualizing; analyzing; recalling; evaluating; inferring

Speaking and Listening: note taking; interpreting special clues; discussing

_____ Bellringer and Grammar Link to the Bellringer, TWE p. 160
_____ Motivating Activity, TWE p. 160

TEACH

Guided Practice

_____ L2, Using the Model, TWE p. 161
_____ L1, Visualizing Dialogue, TWE p. 161
_____ Journal Writing Tip, TWE p. 161
_____ L2, Using the Model, TWE p. 162
_____ Two-Minute Skill Drill, TWE p. 162
_____ Enabling Strategies: LEP, TWE p. 162

Independent Practice

_____ *Fine Art Transparencies, 16–20 **
_____ *Writing Process Transparencies, 14–16B **
_____ *Writing Across the Curriculum, p. 6 **
_____ *Cooperative Learning Activities, pp. 19–24 **
_____ *Thinking and Study Skills, p. 9 **
_____ *Speaking and Listening Activities, p. 23 **
_____ *Composition Practice, p. 28 **

ASSESS

_____ Writing Activities Evaluation Guidelines, TWE p. 163
_____ Using the Grammar Link, TWE p. 163

Reteaching

_____ *Composition Reteaching, p. 28 **

Enrichment

_____ *Composition Enrichment, p. 28 **
_____ *Fine Art Transparencies, 16–20 **
_____ About the Art, TWE p. 163

CLOSE

_____ Close activity, TWE p. 163

* Teacher's Classroom Resources

• *Homework Assignments* •
_____
_____
_____
_____
_____
_____
_____
_____
_____

4.5 Drafting a Story *SE/TWE pp. 164–167*

Teacher's Name _____ Date _____

Grade _____ Class(es) _____ Date(s)_____ M Tu W Th F

FOCUS
LESSON OVERVIEW
Objective: To plan and generate a draft of a brief story
Skills: preparing before writing; constructing a framework for a story; choosing authentic details
Critical Thinking: generating new information; visualizing; identifying main ideas; synthesizing; relating
Speaking and Listening: discussing; note taking; evaluating

_____ Bellringer and Grammar Link to the Bellringer, TWE p. 164
_____ Motivating Activity, TWE p. 164

TEACH
Guided Practice
_____ L2, Using the Model, TWE p. 165
_____ L2, Cooperative Learning, TWE p. 165
_____ Journal Writing Tip, TWE p. 165
_____ L1, Focusing on Drafting Tips, TWE p. 166
_____ Two-Minute Skill Drill, TWE p. 166
_____ Enabling Strategies: LEP, TWE p. 166

Independent Practice
_____ *Fine Art Transparencies*, 16–20 *
_____ *Writing Process Transparencies*, 14–16B *
_____ *Writing Across the Curriculum*, p. 7 *
_____ *Cooperative Learning Activities*, pp. 19–24 *
_____ *Thinking and Study Skills*, p. 8 *
_____ *Sentence Combining Practice*, p. 25 *
_____ *Speaking and Listening Activities*, p. 23 *
_____ *Composition Practice*, p. 29 *

• *Homework Assignments* •

ASSESS
_____ Writing Activities Evaluation Guidelines, TWE p. 167
_____ Using the Grammar Link, TWE p. 167

Reteaching
_____ *Composition Reteaching*, p. 29 *

Enrichment
_____ *Composition Enrichment*, p. 29 *

CLOSE
_____ Close activity, TWE p. 167

* Teacher's Classroom Resources

4.6 Evaluating a Story Opening *SE/TWE pp. 168–171*

Teacher's Name _____ Date _____
Grade _____ Class(es) _____ Date(s)_____ M Tu W Th F

FOCUS
LESSON OVERVIEW
Objective: To explore various methods for beginning a story
Skills: preparing to write; generating and evaluating ideas; choosing the best approach for beginning a particular story
Critical Thinking: evaluating; analyzing; synthesizing; recalling; activating prior knowledge; decision making; establishing and evaluating criteria
Speaking and Listening: discussing; note taking; evaluating; informal speaking; explaining a process

_____ Bellringer and Grammar Link to the Bellringer, TWE p. 168
_____ Motivating Activity, TWE p. 168

TEACH
Guided Practice
_____ L2, Using the Model, TWE p. 169
_____ L3, Promoting Discussion, TWE p. 169
_____ Journal Writing Tip, TWE p. 169
_____ L2, Creating a Story Opening, TWE p. 170
_____ Two-Minute Skill Drill, TWE p. 170
_____ Enabling Strategies: LEP, TWE p. 170

Independent Practice
_____ *Fine Art Transparencies*, 16–20 *
_____ *Writing Process Transparencies*, 14–16B *
_____ *Writing Across the Curriculum*, p. 7 *
_____ *Cooperative Learning Activities*, pp. 19–24 *
_____ *Thinking and Study Skills*, p. 16 *
_____ *Sentence Combining Practice*, p. 25 *
_____ *Speaking and Listening Activities*, p. 23 *
_____ *Composition Practice*, p. 30 *

• Homework Assignments •

ASSESS
_____ Writing Activities Evaluation Guidelines, TWE p. 171
_____ Cross-Curricular: Art, TWE p. 171
_____ Using the Grammar Link, TWE p. 171

Reteaching
_____ *Composition Reteaching*, p. 30 *

Enrichment
_____ *Composition Enrichment*, p. 30 *
_____ *Fine Art Transparencies*, 16–20 *
_____ About the Art, TWE p. 171

CLOSE
_____ Close activity, TWE p. 171

* Teacher's Classroom Resources

4.7 Responding to a Story *SE/TWE pp. 172–175*

Teacher's Name _____ Date _____

Grade _____ Class(es) _____ Date(s)_____ M Tu W Th F

FOCUS
LESSON OVERVIEW
Objective: To respond creatively to a short story
Skills: reading comprehension; writing responses to stories; using apostrophes correctly
Critical Thinking: recalling; evaluating; establishing and evaluating criteria; generating new information
Speaking and Listening: discussing; interviewing; informal speaking

_____ Bellringer and Grammar Link to the Bellringer, TWE p. 172
_____ Motivating Activity, TWE p. 172

TEACH
Guided Practice
_____ L2, Using the Model, TWE p. 173
_____ L3, Reading Book Reviews, TWE p. 173
_____ Journal Writing Tip, TWE p. 173
_____ L2, Responding to Literature, TWE p. 174
_____ Two-Minute Skill Drill, TWE p. 174
_____ Enabling Strategies: LEP, TWE p. 174

Independent Practice
_____ *Fine Art Transparencies, 16–20 **
_____ *Writing Process Transparencies, 14–16B **
_____ *Writing Across the Curriculum, pp. 19–20 **
_____ *Cooperative Learning Activities, pp. 19–24 **
_____ *Thinking and Study Skills, p. 22 **
_____ *Sentence Combining Practice, p. 25 **
_____ *Speaking and Listening Activities, p. 23 **
_____ *Composition Practice, p. 31 **

• Homework Assignments •

_____

_____

_____

_____

_____

_____

_____

_____

ASSESS
_____ Writing Activities Evaluation Guidelines, TWE p. 175
_____ Cross-Curricular: Mythology, TWE p. 175
_____ Using the Grammar Link, TWE p. 175

Reteaching
_____ *Composition Reteaching, p. 31 **

Enrichment
_____ *Composition Enrichment, p. 31 **
_____ *Fine Art Transparencies, 16–20 **
_____ About the Art, TWE p. 175

CLOSE
_____ Close activity, TWE p. 175

* Teacher's Classroom Resources

Unit 4 Writing Process in Action *SE/TWE pp. 176–179*

Teacher's Name _____ Date _____

Grade _____ Class(es) _____ Date(s)_____ M Tu W Th F

FOCUS
LESSON OVERVIEW
Objective: To create a story emphasizing the element of character

Skills: using the five stages of the writing process: prewriting, drafting, revising, editing, and presenting

Critical Thinking: synthesizing; defining and clarifying; recalling

Speaking and Listening: informal speaking; discussing; questioning

_____ Bellringer and Grammar Link to the Bellringer, TWE p. 176

_____ Motivating Activity, TWE p. 176

TEACH
Prewriting
_____ L2, Deciding on Story Ideas, TWE p. 177

_____ *Thinking and Study Skills*, p. 5 *

Drafting
_____ L1, Avoiding Writer's Block, TWE p. 177

Revising
_____ L2, Peer Editing, TWE p. 178

_____ L2, Cooperative Learning, TWE p. 178

Editing
_____ L2, Peer Editing, TWE p. 178

Presenting
_____ Presenting activity, TWE p. 178

_____ Enrichment and Extension, TWE p. 178

_____ Speaking and Listening, TWE p. 179

_____ Journal Writing Tip, TWE p. 179

Independent Practice
_____ *Writing Process Transparencies*, 14–16B *

_____ *Thinking and Study Skills*, p. 5 *

_____ *Sentence Combining Practice*, p. 25 *

_____ *Composition Practice*, p. 32 *

_____ **Grammar Workbook,** Lesson 25

ASSESS
_____ Evaluation Guidelines, TWE p. 179

Reteaching
_____ *Composition Reteaching*, p. 32 *

Enrichment
_____ *Composition Enrichment*, p. 32 *

CLOSE
_____ Close activity, TWE p. 179

* Teacher's Classroom Resources

• Homework Assignments •

_____

_____

_____

_____

_____

_____

_____

_____

Unit 4 Literature: from "A Huge Black Umbrella," Marjorie Agosín *SE/TWE pp. 180–185*

Teacher's Name _____ Date _____

Grade _____ Class(es) _____ Date(s) _____ M Tu W Th F

FOCUS
LESSON OVERVIEW
Objective: To examine and appreciate how a professional writer uses narrative to express events and feelings

Skills: reading comprehension

Critical Thinking: synthesizing

Speaking and Listening: discussing

_____ Bellringer and Motivating Activity, TWE p. 180

TEACH
Guided Practice
_____ L2, Guided Reading, TWE pp. 181–184

_____ Genre and Style, TWE p. 182

_____ Writers and Writing, TWE p. 182

_____ About the Art, TWE p. 183

_____ About the Art, TWE p. 184

_____ Cooperative Learning, TWE p. 185

Independent Practice
_____ *Fine Art Transparencies*, 16–20 *

_____ *Speaking and Listening Activities*, pp. 14–15 *

_____ *Thinking and Study Skills*, p. 22 *

ASSESS
_____ Evaluation Guidelines, TWE p. 185

CLOSE
_____ Close activity, TWE p. 185

* Teacher's Classroom Resources

UNIT 4 REVIEW *p. 186*
_____ Reflecting on the Unit, TWE p. 186

_____ Writing Across the Curriculum, TWE p. 186

_____ Adding to Your Portfolio, TWE p. 186

_____ Portfolio Evaluation, TWE p. 186

• Homework Assignments •

_____

_____

_____

_____

_____

_____

_____

_____

_____

Unit Assessment

_____ *Tests with Answer Key*
Unit 4 Choice A Test, p. 13
Unit 4 Choice B Test, p. 14
Unit 4 Composition Objective
  Test, pp. 15–16

_____ *Test Generator*
Unit 4 Choice A Test
Unit 4 Choice B Test
Unit 4 Composition Objective
  Test

You may wish to administer one of these tests as a mastery test.

Unit 5 Case Study: Expository Writing SE/TWE pp. 188–193

Teacher's Name _____ Date _____

Grade _____ Class(es) _____ Date(s)_____ M Tu W Th F

FOCUS
LESSON OVERVIEW
Objective: To demonstrate the use of expository writing in exhibit information labels
Skills: gathering information; selecting details; examining audience; writing to inform and explain
Critical Thinking: identifying; synthesizing; classifying; relating; identifying main idea; building background
Speaking and Listening: discussing; note taking

_____ Bellringer and Grammar Link to the Bellringer, TWE p. 188
_____ Motivating Activity, TWE p. 188

TEACH
_____ Building Background, TWE p. 189
_____ Preview the Case Study, TWE p. 189
_____ Discussion Prompts, TWE pp. 190, 191
_____ Cultural Diversity, TWE p. 190
_____ Connections Across the Curriculum: Science, TWE p. 191
_____ Visual Thinking, TWE p. 192

Guided Practice
_____ L2, Discussion, TWE p. 192

Independent Practice
_____ *Writing Process Transparencies*, 17–19B *
_____ *Case Studies: Writing in the Real World*, pp. 17–20 *
_____ *Cooperative Learning Activities*, pp. 25–29 *
_____ *Thinking and Study Skills*, pp. 3, 4, 13, 14, 20 *

ASSESS
_____ Responding to the Case Study, TWE p. 193
_____ Using the Grammar Link, TWE p. 193

Reteaching
_____ Reteaching activity, TWE p. 193

Enrichment
_____ Enrichment activity, TWE p. 193

CLOSE
_____ Close activity, TWE p. 193

* Teacher's Classroom Resources

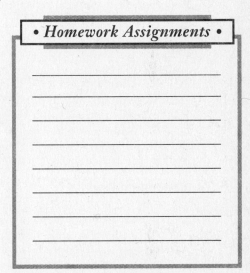

• Homework Assignments •

_____
_____
_____
_____
_____
_____
_____
_____

Unit Assessment

_____ *Tests with Answer Key*
Unit 5 Choice A Test, p. 17
Unit 5 Choice B Test, p. 18
Unit 5 Composition Objective
  Test, pp. 19–20
_____ *Test Generator*
Unit 5 Choice A Test
Unit 5 Choice B Test
Unit 5 Composition Objective
  Test
You may wish to administer either the
Unit 5 Choice A Test or the Unit 5
Choice B Test as a pretest.

5.1 Giving Information and Explanations

SE/TWE pp. 194–197

Teacher's Name _____ Date _____

Grade _____ Class(es) _____ Date(s) _____ M Tu W Th F

FOCUS
LESSON OVERVIEW
Objective: To explain and inform, using details and observing the qualities of good writing
Skills: brainstorming; evaluating sources of information; using supporting facts to explain and inform; ordering the steps in a process
Critical Thinking: evaluating; analyzing; activating prior knowledge; establishing and evaluating criteria
Speaking and Listening: discussing; note taking; evaluating; informal speaking; explaining a process

_____ Bellringer and Grammar Link to the Bellringer, TWE p. 194
_____ Motivating Activity, TWE p. 194

TEACH
Guided Practice
_____ L2, Using the Model, TWE p. 195
_____ Two-Minute Skill Drill, TWE p. 195
_____ Journal Writing Tip, TWE p. 195
_____ L3, Gathering Information, TWE p. 196
_____ Two-Minute Skill Drill, TWE p. 196
_____ Enabling Strategies: LEP, TWE p. 196

Independent Practice
_____ *Fine Art Transparencies*, 21–25 *
_____ *Writing Process Transparencies*, 17–19B *
_____ *Cooperative Learning Activities*, pp. 25–30 *
_____ *Writing Across the Curriculum*, p. 13 *
_____ *Sentence Combining Practice*, pp. 30–32 *
_____ *Thinking and Study Skills*, pp. 3, 5, 17–18 *
_____ *Speaking and Listening Activities*, pp. 12–13, 21, 23 *
_____ *Research Paper and Report Writing*, pp. 33–34, 36, 38 *
_____ *Composition Practice*, p. 33 *

ASSESS
_____ Writing Activities Evaluation Guidelines, TWE p. 197
_____ Cross-Curricular: Science, TWE p. 197
_____ Using the Grammar Link, TWE p. 197

Reteaching
_____ *Composition Reteaching*, p. 33 *

Enrichment
_____ *Composition Enrichment*, p. 33 *
_____ *Fine Art Transparencies*, 21–25 *
_____ About the Art, TWE p. 197

CLOSE
_____ Close activity, TWE p. 197

* Teacher's Classroom Resources

• Homework Assignments •

_____
_____
_____
_____
_____
_____
_____
_____
_____

Unit Assessment

_____ *Tests with Answer Key*
Unit 5 Choice A Test, p. 17
Unit 5 Choice B Test, p. 18
Unit 5 Composition Objective
Test, pp. 19–20
_____ *Test Generator*
Unit 5 Choice A Test
Unit 5 Choice B Test
Unit 5 Composition Objective
Test
You may wish to administer either the Unit 5 Choice A Test or the Unit 5 Choice B Test as a pretest.

5.2 Organizing Informative Writing *SE/TWE pp. 198–201*

Teacher's Name _____ Date _____

Grade _____ Class(es) _____ Date(s) _____ M Tu W Th F

FOCUS
LESSON OVERVIEW
Objective: To organize details for informative writing
Skills: organizing information; understanding kinds of details; using details
Critical Thinking: decision making; categorizing; defining and clarifying
Speaking and Listening: discussing

_____ Bellringer and Grammar Link to the Bellringer, TWE p. 198
_____ Motivating Activity, TWE p. 198

TEACH
Guided Practice
_____ L2, Organizing Visually, TWE p. 199
_____ Two-Minute Skill Drill, TWE p. 199
_____ Journal Writing Tip, TWE p. 199
_____ L2, Using the Model, TWE p. 200
_____ L2, Distinguishing Between Reasons and Examples, TWE p. 200
_____ Enabling Strategies: LEP, TWE p. 200

Independent Practice
_____ *Fine Art Transparencies*, 21–25 *
_____ *Writing Process Transparencies*, 17–19B *
_____ *Writing Across the Curriculum*, pp. 17, 22 *
_____ *Cooperative Learning Activities*, pp. 25–30 *
_____ *Thinking and Study Skills*, pp. 8, 10–11 *
_____ *Sentence Combining Practice*, pp. 30–32 *
_____ *Speaking and Listening Activities*, pp. 12–13, 21, 23 *
_____ *Research Paper and Report Writing*, pp. 33–34, 36, 38 *
_____ *Composition Practice*, p. 34 *

ASSESS
_____ Writing Activities Evaluation Guidelines, TWE p. 201
_____ Using the Grammar Link, TWE p. 201

Reteaching
_____ *Composition Reteaching*, p. 34 *

Enrichment
_____ *Composition Enrichment*, p. 34 *

CLOSE
_____ Close activity, TWE p. 201

* Teacher's Classroom Resources

• Homework Assignments •

_____

_____

_____

_____

_____

_____

_____

_____

5.3 Writing About Similarities and Differences

SE/TWE pp. 202–205

Teacher's Name _____ Date _____

Grade _____ Class(es) _____ Date(s)_____ M Tu W Th F

FOCUS
LESSON OVERVIEW
Objective: To compare and contrast two subjects

Skills: making observations; constructing a chart before drafting; relating things on the basis of differences and similarities

Critical Thinking: analyzing; synthesizing; relating; activating prior knowledge; visualizing; generating new information

Speaking and Listening: discussing; asking questions; evaluating; informal speaking

_____ Bellringer and Grammar Link to the Bellringer, TWE p. 202
_____ Motivating Activity, TWE p. 202

TEACH
Guided Practice
_____ L2, Using the Model, TWE p. 203
_____ L1, Discussing Comparison and Contrast, TWE p. 203
_____ Journal Writing Tip, TWE p. 203
_____ L2, Using the Model, TWE p. 204
_____ Two-Minute Skill Drill, TWE p. 204
_____ Enabling Strategies: LEP, TWE p. 204

Independent Practice
_____ *Fine Art Transparencies, 21–25 **
_____ *Writing Process Transparencies, 17–19B **
_____ *Cooperative Learning Activities, pp. 25–30 **
_____ *Writing Across the Curriculum, p. 23 **
_____ *Research Paper and Report Writing, pp. 33–34, 36, 38 **
_____ *Thinking and Study Skills, pp. 6, 8–9, 11 **
_____ *Sentence Combining Practice, pp. 30–32 **
_____ *Speaking and Listening Activities, pp. 12–13, 21, 23 **
_____ *Composition Practice, p. 15 **

ASSESS
_____ Writing Activities Evaluation Guidelines, TWE p. 205
_____ Cross-Curricular: Art, TWE p. 205
_____ Using the Grammar Link, TWE p. 205

Reteaching
_____ *Composition Reteaching, p. 35 **

Enrichment
_____ *Composition Enrichment, p. 35 **
_____ *Fine Art Transparencies, 21–25 **
_____ About the Art, TWE p. 205

CLOSE
_____ Close activity, TWE p. 205

* Teacher's Classroom Resources

> **• Homework Assignments •**
>
> _____
> _____
> _____
> _____
> _____
> _____
> _____
> _____
> _____

5.4 Explaining How Something Works

SE/TWE pp. 206–209

Teacher's Name _____ Date _____

Grade _____ Class(es) _____ Date(s)_____ M Tu W Th F

FOCUS
LESSON OVERVIEW
Objective: To write a clear and well-ordered explanation
Skills: putting steps in order; using transition words; using precise verbs
Critical Thinking: recalling; summarizing; analyzing; visualizing
Speaking and Listening: evaluating; explaining process; group discussion

_____ Bellringer and Grammar Link to the Bellringer, TWE p. 206
_____ Motivating Activity, TWE p. 206

TEACH
Guided Practice
_____ L2, Using the Model, TWE p. 207
_____ L1, Examining a Process, TWE p. 207
_____ Journal Writing Tip, TWE p. 207
_____ L2, Revising Directions, TWE p. 208
_____ Two-Minute Skill Drill, TWE p. 208
_____ Enabling Strategies: LEP, TWE p. 208

Independent Practice
_____ *Fine Art Transparencies, 21–25 ***
_____ *Writing Process Transparencies, 17–19B ***
_____ *Writing Across the Curriculum, p. 17 ***
_____ *Cooperative Learning Activities, pp. 25–30 ***
_____ *Composition Practice, p. 36 ***
_____ *Thinking and Study Skills, pp. 8–9, 11 ***
_____ *Sentence Combining Practice, p. 30–32 ***
_____ *Speaking and Listening Activities, pp. 12–13, 21, 23 ***
_____ *Research Paper and Report Writing, pp. 33–34, 36, 38 ***

ASSESS
_____ Writing Activities Evaluation Guidelines, TWE p. 209
_____ Using the Grammar Link, TWE p. 209

Reteaching
_____ *Composition Reteaching, p. 36 ***

Enrichment
_____ *Composition Enrichment, p. 36 ***

CLOSE
_____ Close activity, TWE p. 209

* Teacher's Classroom Resources

• Homework Assignments •

_____
_____
_____
_____
_____
_____
_____
_____

5.5 Identifying Cause and Effect *SE/TWE pp. 210–213*

Teacher's Name _____ Date _____

Grade _____ Class(es) _____ Date(s)_____ M Tu W Th F

FOCUS
LESSON OVERVIEW
Objective: To identify and analyze cause-and-effect relationships
Skills: identifying cause-and-effect relationships; analyzing cause-and-effect events; examining how one effect leads to another
Critical Thinking: analyzing; relating cause-and-effect; evaluating
Speaking and Listening: discussing; evaluating; questioning

_____ Bellringer and Grammar Link to the Bellringer, TWE p. 210
_____ Motivating Activity, TWE p. 210

TEACH
Guided Practice
_____ L2, Using the Model, TWE p. 211
_____ L1, Discussing Causes, TWE p. 211
_____ Journal Writing Tip, TWE p. 211
_____ L2, Using the Model, TWE p. 212
_____ L3, Analyzing Advertisements and Commercials, TWE p. 212
_____ Two-Minute Skill Drill, TWE p. 212
_____ Enabling Strategies: LEP, TWE p. 212

Independent Practice
_____ *Fine Art Transparencies*, 21–25 *
_____ *Writing Process Transparencies*, 17–19B *
_____ *Cooperative Learning Activities*, pp. 25–30 *
_____ *Writing Across the Curriculum*, p. 12 *
_____ *Research Paper and Report Writing*, pp. 33–34, 36, 38 *
_____ *Thinking and Study Skills*, pp. 3–4, 8, 10 *
_____ *Sentence Combining Practice*, pp. 30–32 *
_____ *Speaking and Listening Activities*, pp. 12–13, 21, 23 *
_____ *Composition Practice*, p. 37 *

ASSESS
_____ Writing Activities Evaluation Guidelines, TWE p. 213
_____ Cross-Curricular: History, TWE p. 213
_____ Using the Grammar Link, TWE p. 213

Reteaching
_____ *Composition Reteaching*, p. 37 *

Enrichment
_____ *Composition Enrichment*, p. 37 *
_____ *Fine Art Transparencies*, 21–25 *
_____ About the Art, TWE p. 213

• Homework Assignments •

_____

_____

_____

_____

_____

_____

_____

_____

CLOSE
_____ Close activity, TWE p. 213

* Teacher's Classroom Resources

5.6 Reports: Narrowing a Topic *SE/TWE pp. 214–217*

Teacher's Name _____ Date _____

Grade _____ Class(es) _____ Date(s)_____ M Tu W Th F

FOCUS
LESSON OVERVIEW
Objective: To narrow an expository writing topic and to direct the topic toward the intended audience
Skills: narrowing a topic; tailoring writing to an audience
Critical Thinking: recalling; relating topics and subtopics; building background; generating new information
Speaking and Listening: informal speaking; discussing; questioning

_____ Bellringer and Grammar Link to the Bellringer, TWE p. 214
_____ Motivating Activity, TWE p. 214

TEACH
Guided Practice
_____ L2, Identifying Subtopics, TWE p. 215
_____ Two-Minute Skill Drill, TWE p. 215
_____ Journal Writing Tip, TWE p. 215
_____ L2, Using the Model, TWE p. 216
_____ L3, Examining Writing for Different Audiences, TWE p. 216
_____ Enabling Strategies: LEP, TWE p. 216

Independent Practice
_____ *Fine Art Transparencies, 21–25 **
_____ *Writing Process Transparencies, 17–19B **
_____ *Writing Across the Curriculum, p. 6 **
_____ *Cooperative Learning Activities, pp. 25–30 **
_____ *Thinking and Study Skills, pp. 7–9 **
_____ *Sentence Combining Practice, pp. 30–32 **
_____ *Speaking and Listening Activities, pp. 12–13, 21, 23 **
_____ *Research Paper and Report Writing, pp. 33–34, 36, 38 **
_____ *Composition Practice, p. 38 **

ASSESS
_____ Writing Activities Evaluation Guidelines, TWE p. 217
_____ Using the Grammar Link, TWE p. 217

Reteaching
_____ *Composition Reteaching, p. 38 **

Enrichment
_____ *Composition Enrichment, p. 38 **
_____ *Fine Art Transparencies, 21–25 **
_____ About the Art, TWE p. 217

CLOSE
_____ Close activity, TWE p. 217

* Teacher's Classroom Resources

• Homework Assignments •

_____
_____
_____
_____
_____
_____
_____
_____
_____

5.7 Reports: Turning to Helpful Sources

SE/TWE pp. 218–221

Teacher's Name _____ Date _____

Grade _____ Class(es) _____ Date(s)_____ M Tu W Th F

FOCUS

LESSON OVERVIEW

Objective: To establish and assess criteria for choosing useful sources of reference, and to write meaningful notes on a topic

Skills: choosing among resources; taking meaningful notes

Critical Thinking: analyzing; evaluating; summarizing; decision making; generating new information

Speaking and Listening: discussing; informal speaking; oral reporting

_____ Bellringer and Grammar Link to the Bellringer, TWE p. 218
_____ Motivating Activity, TWE p. 218

TEACH

Guided Practice

_____ L2, Narrowing a Topic and Clarifying Research, TWE p. 219
_____ L1, Seeking Help in the Library, TWE p. 219
_____ Journal Writing Tip, TWE p. 219
_____ L2, Using Note Cards, TWE p. 220
_____ Two-Minute Skill Drill, TWE p. 220
_____ Enabling Strategies: LEP, TWE p. 220

Independent Practice

_____ *Fine Art Transparencies, 21–25 **
_____ *Writing Process Transparencies, 17–19B **
_____ *Writing Across the Curriculum, p. 7 **
_____ *Cooperative Learning Activities, pp. 25–30 **
_____ *Research Paper and Report Writing, pp. 33–34, 36, 38 **
_____ *Thinking and Study Skills, pp. 4–5, 20, 23–24, 35–36 **
_____ *Sentence Combining Practice, pp. 30–32 **
_____ *Speaking and Listening Activities, p. 12–13, 21, 23 **
_____ *Composition Practice, p. 39 **

ASSESS

_____ Writing Activities Evaluation Guidelines, TWE p. 221
_____ Cross-Curricular, TWE p. 221
_____ Using the Grammar Link, TWE p. 221

Reteaching

_____ *Composition Reteaching, p. 39 **

Enrichment

_____ *Composition Enrichment, p. 39 **

CLOSE

_____ Close activity, TWE p. 221

* Teacher's Classroom Resources

• Homework Assignments •

_____
_____
_____
_____
_____
_____
_____
_____
_____

5.8 Reports: Conducting an Interview

SE/TWE pp. 222–225

Teacher's Name _____ Date _____

Grade _____ Class(es) _____ Date(s)_____ M Tu W Th F

FOCUS
LESSON OVERVIEW
Objective: To prepare for and conduct an interview to gather information for a report
Skills: preparing for an interview; conducting an interview
Critical Thinking: summarizing; generating questions; identifying; establishing and evaluating criteria
Speaking and Listening: note taking; interviewing; discussing; questioning

_____ Bellringer and Grammar Link to the Bellringer, TWE p. 222
_____ Motivating Activity, TWE p. 222

TEACH
Guided Practice
_____ L2, Using the Model, TWE p. 223
_____ Two-Minute Skill Drill, TWE p. 223
_____ Journal Writing Tip, TWE p. 223
_____ L2, Using a Videotape, TWE p. 224
_____ L3, Discussing Techniques, TWE p. 224
_____ Enabling Strategies: LEP, TWE p. 224

Independent Practice
_____ *Fine Art Transparencies*, 21–25 *
_____ *Writing Across the Curriculum*, p. 16 *
_____ *Cooperative Learning Activities*, pp. 25–30 *
_____ *Thinking and Study Skills*, pp. 2, 4, 33–34 *
_____ *Sentence Combining Practice*, pp. 30–32 *
_____ *Speaking and Listening Activities*, pp. 12–13, 21, 23 *
_____ *Research Paper and Report Writing*, pp. 33–34, 36, 38 *
_____ *Composition Practice*, p. 40 *

• Homework Assignments •

ASSESS
_____ Writing Activities Evaluation Guidelines, TWE p. 225
_____ Using the Grammar Link, TWE p. 225

Reteaching
_____ *Composition Reteaching*, p. 40 *

Enrichment
_____ *Composition Enrichment*, p. 40 *

CLOSE
_____ Close activity, TWE p. 225

* Teacher's Classroom Resources

5.9 Reports: Organizing and Drafting

SE/TWE pp. 226–229

Teacher's Name _____ Date _____

Grade _____ Class(es) _____ Date(s)_____ M Tu W Th F

FOCUS
LESSON OVERVIEW
Objective: To focus and organize information and present research effectively
Skills: stating a main idea; outlining; identifying the introduction, body, and conclusion of a report
Critical Thinking: summarizing; identifying main idea; decision making
Speaking and Listening: discussing; evaluating; questioning

_____ Bellringer and Grammar Link to the Bellringer, TWE p. 226
_____ Motivating Activity, TWE p. 226

TEACH
Guided Practice
_____ L2, Understanding Main Idea, TWE p. 227
_____ L1, Using an Outline, TWE p. 227
_____ Journal Writing Tip, TWE p. 227
_____ L2, Cooperative Learning, TWE p. 228
_____ Two-Minute Skill Drill, TWE p. 228
_____ Enabling Strategies: LEP, TWE p. 228

Independent Practice
_____ *Fine Art Transparencies, 21–25 **
_____ *Cooperative Learning Activities, pp. 25–30 **
_____ *Writing Across the Curriculum, p. 7 **
_____ *Thinking and Study Skills, pp. 4, 13, 15, 21 **
_____ *Sentence Combining Practice, pp. 30–32 **
_____ *Speaking and Listening Activities, pp. 12–13, 21, 23 **
_____ *Research Paper and Report Writing, pp. 33–34, 36, 38 **
_____ *Composition Practice, p. 41 **

ASSESS
_____ Writing Activities Evaluation Guidelines, TWE p. 229
_____ Using the Grammar Link, TWE p. 229

Reteaching
_____ *Composition Reteaching, p. 41 **

Enrichment
_____ *Composition Enrichment, p. 41 **

CLOSE
_____ Close activity, TWE p. 229

* Teacher's Classroom Resources

• Homework Assignments •

_____
_____
_____
_____
_____
_____
_____
_____
_____

5.10 Reports: Revising and Presenting

SE/TWE pp. 230–233

Teacher's Name _____ Date _____

Grade _____ Class(es) _____ Date(s) _____ M Tu W Th F

FOCUS
LESSON OVERVIEW
Objective: To revise a written report
Skills: checking for errors; using irregular verbs correctly; improving past work; sharing written work
Critical Thinking: analyzing; recalling; evaluating; defining and clarifying
Speaking and Listening: discussing; evaluating; oral reporting

_____ Bellringer and Grammar Link to the Bellringer, TWE p. 230
_____ Motivating Activity, TWE p. 230

TEACH
Guided Practice
_____ L2, Using the Model, TWE p. 231
_____ L1, Checking Work in Steps, TWE p. 231
_____ Two-Minute Skill Drill, TWE p. 231
_____ Journal Writing Tip, TWE p. 231
_____ L2, Cooperative Learning, TWE p. 232
_____ L2, Analyzing Illustration, TWE p. 232
_____ Enabling Strategies: LEP, TWE p. 232

Independent Practice
_____ *Fine Art Transparencies, 21–25 **
_____ *Writing Process Transparencies, 17–19B **
_____ *Cooperative Learning Activities, pp. 25–30 **
_____ *Speaking and Listening Activities, pp. 12–13, 21, 23 **
_____ *Sentence Combining Practice, pp. 30–32 **
_____ *Thinking and Study Skills, pp. 4, 13–14, 20–21 **
_____ *Research Paper and Report Writing, pp. 33–34, 36, 38 **
_____ *Composition Practice, p. 42 **

ASSESS
_____ Writing Activities Evaluation Guidelines, TWE p. 233
_____ Using the Grammar Link, TWE p. 233

Reteaching
_____ *Composition Reteaching, p. 42 **

Enrichment
_____ *Composition Enrichment, p. 42 **
_____ *Fine Art Transparencies, 21–25 **
_____ About the Art, TWE p. 233

CLOSE
_____ Close activity, TWE p. 233

* Teacher's Classroom Resources

> ### • Homework Assignments •
>
> _____
> _____
> _____
> _____
> _____
> _____
> _____
> _____

5.11 Comparing Two People *SE/TWE pp. 234–237*

Teacher's Name _____ Date _____

Grade _____ Class(es) _____ Date(s)_____ M Tu W Th F

FOCUS

LESSON OVERVIEW

Objective: To effectively compare people in writing
Skills: charting a comparison; making a Venn diagram; comparing real and fictional characters
Critical Thinking: contrasting; comparing; recalling; making inferences
Speaking and Listening: reading aloud; discussing

_____ Bellringer and Grammar Link to the Bellringer, TWE p. 234
_____ Motivating Activity, TWE p. 234

TEACH

Guided Practice

_____ L2, Using the Model, TWE p. 235
_____ L1, Recording Information, TWE p. 235
_____ Journal Writing Tip, TWE p. 235
_____ L2, Cooperative Learning, TWE p. 236
_____ Two-Minute Skill Drill, TWE p. 236
_____ Enabling Strategies: LEP, TWE p. 236

Independent Practice

_____ *Fine Art Transparencies*, 21–25 *
_____ *Writing Process Transparencies*, 17–19B *
_____ *Writing Across the Curriculum*, p. 18 *
_____ *Cooperative Learning Activities*, pp. 25–30 *
_____ *Thinking and Study Skills*, pp. 6, 8, 15 *
_____ *Sentence Combining Practice*, pp. 30–32 *
_____ *Speaking and Listening Activities*, pp. 12–13, 21, 23 *
_____ *Research Paper and Report Writing*, pp. 33–34, 36, 38 *
_____ *Composition Practice*, p. 43 *

• Homework Assignments •

_____
_____
_____
_____
_____
_____
_____
_____

ASSESS

_____ Writing Activities Evaluation Guidelines, TWE p. 237
_____ Using the Grammar Link, TWE p. 237

Reteaching

_____ *Composition Reteaching*, p. 43 *

Enrichment

_____ *Composition Enrichment*, p. 43 *

CLOSE

_____ Close activity, TWE p. 237

* Teacher's Classroom Resources

Unit 5 Writing Process in Action *SE/TWE pp. 238–241*

Teacher's Name _____ Date _____

Grade _____ Class(es) _____ Date(s)_____ M Tu W Th F

FOCUS
LESSON OVERVIEW
Objective: To write a guide to the diverse population of one's own town or city

Skills: using the five stages of the writing process: prewriting, drafting, revising, editing, and presenting

Critical Thinking: analyzing; visualizing; generating new information; patterning

Speaking and Listening: note taking; discussing; questioning

_____ Bellringer and Grammar Link to the Bellringer, TWE p. 238

_____ Motivating Activity, TWE p. 238

TEACH
Prewriting
_____ L2, Developing Ideas for Expository Writing, TWE p. 239

Drafting
_____ L1, Organizing Information, TWE p. 239

Revising
_____ L2, Peer Editing, TWE p. 240

Editing
_____ L2, Peer Editing, TWE p. 240

Presenting
_____ Presenting activity, TWE p. 240

_____ Journal Writing Tip, TWE p. 240

_____ Enrichment and Extension, TWE p. 240

_____ Enrichment and Extension, TWE p. 241

Independent Practice
_____ *Writing Process Transparencies,* 17–19B *

_____ *Thinking and Study Skills,* pp. 3–5, 7–9, 20, 23–24, 34–35 *

_____ *Sentence Combining Practice,* p. 30–32 *

_____ *Composition Practice,* p. 44 *

_____ **Grammar Workbook,** Lessons 68–71, 86–92

ASSESS
_____ Evaluation Guidelines, TWE p. 241

Reteaching
_____ *Composition Reteaching,* p. 44 *

Enrichment
_____ *Composition Enrichment,* p. 44 *

CLOSE
_____ Close activity, TWE p. 241

* Teacher's Classroom Resources

• Homework Assignments •

_____

_____

_____

_____

_____

_____

_____

_____

Unit 5 Literature: from *Living Treasure*, Laurence Pringle *SE/TWE pp. 242–247*

Teacher's Name _____ Date _____

Grade _____ Class(es) _____ Date(s)_____ M Tu W Th F

FOCUS
LESSON OVERVIEW
Objective: To analyze the techniques the author uses to convey the diversity of life on our planet
Skills: reading comprehension
Critical Thinking: analyzing; classifying; defining and clarifying
Speaking and Listening: discussing

_____ Bellringer and Motivating Activity, TWE p. 242

TEACH
Guided Practice
_____ L2, Guided Reading, TWE pp. 243–246
_____ About the Art, TWE p. 243
_____ About the Art, TWE p. 244
_____ Genre and Style, TWE p. 244
_____ Writers and Writing, TWE p. 245
_____ Connections Across the Curriculum: Health, TWE p. 246
_____ Enabling Strategies: LEP, TWE p. 247

Independent Practice
_____ *Fine Art Transparencies*, 21–25 *
_____ *Speaking and Listening Activities*, pp. 10–11, 21 *
_____ *Thinking and Study Skills*, pp.3–4, 7–9, 20 *

ASSESS
_____ Evaluation Guidelines for Discussion, TWE p. 247

CLOSE
_____ Close activity, TWE p. 247

* Teacher's Classroom Resources

UNIT 5 REVIEW *p. 248*
_____ Reflecting on the Unit, TWE p. 248
_____ Writing Across the Curriculum, TWE p. 248
_____ Adding to Your Portfolio, TWE p. 248
_____ Portfolio Evaluation, TWE p. 248

• Homework Assignments •

_____
_____
_____
_____
_____
_____
_____
_____

Unit Assessment

_____ *Tests with Answer Key*
Unit 5 Choice A Test, p. 17
Unit 5 Choice B Test, p. 18
Unit 5 Composition Objective
Test, pp. 19–20
_____ *Test Generator*
Unit 5 Choice A Test
Unit 5 Choice B Test
Unit 5 Composition Objective
Test
You may wish to administer one of
these tests as a mastery test.

Unit 6 Case Study: Persuasive Writing *SE/TWE pp. 250–255*

Teacher's Name _____ Date _____

Grade _____ Class(es) _____ Date(s)_____ M Tu W Th F

FOCUS
LESSON OVERVIEW
Objective: To understand how the writing process is used in speech writing, and to develop a position for a debate

Skills: forming a position; preparing arguments; presenting a speech

Critical Thinking: recalling; defining and clarifying; analyzing; generating new information

Speaking and Listening: formal speaking; discussing; process explanation

_____ Bellringer and Grammar Link to the Bellringer, TWE p. 250
_____ Motivating Activity, TWE p. 250

TEACH
_____ Building Background, TWE p. 251
_____ Preview the Case Study, TWE p. 251
_____ Discussion Prompts, TWE pp. 252, 253
_____ Cultural Diversity, TWE p. 252
_____ Connections Across the Curriculum: Science, TWE p. 253
_____ Thinking Skills, TWE p. 254

Guided Practice
_____ L2, Discussion, TWE p. 254

Independent Practice
_____ *Writing Process Transparencies*, 20–22B *
_____ *Cooperative Learning Activities*, pp. 31–36 *
_____ *Case Studies: Writing in the Real World*, pp. 21–24 *
_____ *Thinking and Study Skills*, pp. 4, 5, 11, 14–19 *

ASSESS
_____ Responding to the Case Study, TWE p. 255
_____ Using the Grammar Link, TWE p. 255

Reteaching
_____ Reteaching activity, TWE p. 255

Enrichment
_____ Enrichment activity, TWE p. 255

CLOSE
_____ Close activity, TWE p. 255

* Teacher's Classroom Resources

• Homework Assignments •

_____
_____
_____
_____
_____
_____
_____
_____

Unit Assessment

_____ *Tests with Answer Key*
Unit 6 Choice A Test, p. 21
Unit 6 Choice B Test, p. 22
Unit 6 Composition Objective
Test, pp. 23–24
_____ *Test Generator*
Unit 6 Choice A Test
Unit 6 Choice B Test
Unit 6 Composition Objective
Test
You may wish to administer either the Unit 6 Choice A Test or the Unit 6 Choice B Test as a pretest.

6.1 Using Persuasive Writing *SE/TWE pp. 256–259*

Teacher's Name _____ Date _____

Grade _____ Class(es) _____ Date(s)_____ M Tu W Th F

FOCUS

LESSON OVERVIEW

Objective: To identify common sources of persuasive writing; to observe the importance of word choice in effective persuasion

Skills: understanding a writer's purpose; choosing effective, persuasive words; appealing to readers' emotions

Critical Thinking: analyzing; evaluating; identifying

Speaking and Listening: discussing in small groups; listening to appeals

_____ Bellringer and Grammar Link to the Bellringer, TWE p. 256
_____ Motivating Activity, TWE p. 256

TEACH

Guided Practice

_____ L2, Using the Model, TWE p. 257
_____ L2, Using the Model, TWE p. 257
_____ Two-Minute Skill Drill, TWE p. 257
_____ Journal Writing Tip, TWE p. 257
_____ L2, Using Cooperative Learning, TWE p. 258
_____ L1, Understanding Purpose, TWE p. 258
_____ Enabling Strategies: LEP, TWE p. 258

Independent Practice

_____ *Fine Art Transparencies, 26–30 **
_____ *Writing Process Transparencies, 20–22B **
_____ *Writing Across the Curriculum, pp. 10, 21, 24 **
_____ *Cooperative Learning Activities, pp. 31–36 **
_____ *Thinking and Study Skills, pp. 1–5, 13–14, 19 **
_____ *Speaking and Listening Activities, p. 22 **
_____ *Sentence Combining Practice, pp. 33–35 **
_____ *Composition Practice, p. 45 **

ASSESS

_____ Writing Activities Evaluation Guidelines, TWE p. 259
_____ Using the Grammar Link, TWE p. 259

Reteaching

_____ *Composition Reteaching, p. 45 **

Enrichment

_____ *Composition Enrichment, p. 45 **
_____ *Fine Art Transparencies, 26–30 **

CLOSE

_____ Close activity, TWE p. 259

* Teacher's Classroom Resources

• Homework Assignments •

_____
_____
_____
_____
_____
_____
_____
_____
_____

Unit Assessment

_____ *Tests with Answer Key*
Unit 6 Choice A Test, p. 21
Unit 6 Choice B Test, p. 22
Unit 6 Composition Objective
    Test, pp. 23–24
_____ *Test Generator*
Unit 6 Choice A Test
Unit 6 Choice B Test
Unit 6 Composition Objective
    Test
You may wish to administer either the Unit 6 Choice A Test or the Unit 6 Choice B Test as a pretest.

6.2 Forming an Opinion *SE/TWE pp. 260–263*

Teacher's Name _____ Date _____
Grade _____ Class(es) _____ Date(s) _____ M Tu W Th F

FOCUS
LESSON OVERVIEW
Objective: To define and clarify a position on a topic
Skills: choosing a topic; examining an issue; choosing a position
Critical Thinking: analyzing; recalling; evaluating
Speaking and Listening: speaking and listening in class discussions

_____ Bellringer and Grammar Link to the Bellringer, TWE p. 260
_____ Motivating Activity, TWE p. 260

TEACH
Guided Practice
_____ L2, Using the Model, TWE p. 261
_____ L1, Choosing a Topic, TWE p. 261
_____ Two-Minute Skill Drill, TWE p. 261
_____ Journal Writing Tip, TWE p. 261
_____ L2, Drawing Conclusions, TWE p. 262
_____ L1, Talking About a Topic, TWE p. 262
_____ Enabling Strategies: LEP, TWE p. 262

Independent Practice
_____ *Fine Art Transparencies,* 26–30 *
_____ *Writing Process Transparencies,* 20–22B *
_____ *Writing Across the Curriculum,* pp. 10, 21, 24 *
_____ *Cooperative Learning Activities,* pp. 31–36 *
_____ *Thinking and Study Skills,* pp. 11, 13 *
_____ *Sentence Combining Practice,* pp. 33–35 *
_____ *Speaking and Listening Activities,* p. 22 *
_____ *Composition Practice,* p. 46 *

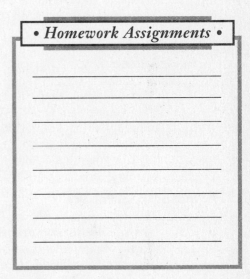

• *Homework Assignments* •

ASSESS
_____ Writing Activities Evaluation Guidelines, TWE p. 263
_____ Cross-Curricular: History, TWE p. 263
_____ Using the Grammar Link, TWE p. 263

Reteaching
_____ *Composition Reteaching,* p. 46 *

Enrichment
_____ *Composition Enrichment,* p. 46 *
_____ *Fine Art Transparencies,* 26–30 *
_____ About the Art, TWE p. 263

CLOSE
_____ Close activity, TWE p. 263

* Teacher's Classroom Resources

6.3 Gathering Evidence *SE/TWE pp. 264–267*

Teacher's Name _____ Date _____

Grade _____ Class(es) _____ Date(s) _____ M Tu W Th F

FOCUS

LESSON OVERVIEW

Objective: To write a proposal to persuade

Skills: finding and using facts, statistics, examples, and reasons to support a position; considering an audience

Critical Thinking: identifying; analyzing; evaluating; classifying

Speaking and Listening: speaking and listening in class discussions

_____ Bellringer and Grammar Link to the Bellringer, TWE p. 264

_____ Motivating Activity, TWE p. 264

TEACH

Guided Practice

_____ L2, Cooperative Learning, TWE p. 265

_____ L3, Considering Opposition, TWE p. 265

_____ Two-Minute Skill Drill, TWE p. 265

_____ Journal Writing Tip, TWE p. 265

_____ L2, Generating Information, TWE p. 266

_____ L1, Considering the Audience, TWE p. 266

_____ Enabling Strategies: LEP, TWE p. 266

Independent Practice

_____ *Fine Art Transparencies*, 26–30 *

_____ *Writing Process Transparencies*, 20–22B *

_____ *Writing Across the Curriculum*, pp. 10, 21, 24 *

_____ *Cooperative Learning Activities*, pp. 31–36 *

_____ *Thinking and Study Skills*, pp. 13–14, 17, 23–24 *

_____ *Sentence Combining Practice*, pp. 33–35 *

_____ *Speaking and Listening Activities*, p. 22 *

_____ *Composition Practice*, p. 47 *

• Homework Assignments •

ASSESS

_____ Writing Activities Evaluation Guidelines, TWE p. 267

_____ Cross-Curricular: Art, TWE p. 267

_____ Using the Grammar Link, TWE p. 267

Reteaching

_____ *Composition Reteaching*, p. 47 *

Enrichment

_____ *Composition Enrichment*, p. 47 *

_____ *Fine Art Transparencies*, 26–30 *

_____ About the Art, TWE p. 267

CLOSE

_____ Close activity, TWE p. 267

* Teacher's Classroom Resources

6.4 Developing an Argument *SE/TWE pp. 268–271*

Teacher's Name _____ Date _____

Grade _____ Class(es) _____ Date(s) _____ M Tu W Th F

FOCUS
LESSON OVERVIEW
Objective: To synthesize evidence into a convincing argument
Skills: stating a position; organizing an argument; writing an editorial
Critical Thinking: identifying; analyzing; classifying; supporting main ideas
Speaking and Listening: speaking and listening in class discussions

_____ Bellringer and Grammar Link to the Bellringer, TWE p. 268
_____ Motivating Activity, TWE p. 268

TEACH
Guided Practice
_____ L2, Using the Model, TWE p. 269
_____ L1, Using the Model, TWE p. 269
_____ Two-Minute Skill Drill, TWE p. 269
_____ Journal Writing Tip, TWE p. 269
_____ L2, Promoting Discussion, TWE p. 270
_____ L1, Identifying the Main Idea, TWE p. 270
_____ Enabling Strategies: LEP, TWE p. 270

Independent Practice
_____ *Fine Art Transparencies*, 26–30 *
_____ *Writing Process Transparencies*, 20–22B *
_____ *Writing Across the Curriculum*, pp. 10, 21, 24 *
_____ *Cooperative Learning Activities*, pp. 31–36 *
_____ *Thinking and Study Skills*, pp. 13, 17, 19 *
_____ *Sentence Combining Practice*, pp. 33–35 *
_____ *Speaking and Listening Activities*, p. 22 *
_____ *Composition Practice*, p. 48 *

ASSESS
_____ Writing Activities Evaluation Guidelines, TWE p. 271
_____ Cross-Curricular: Music, TWE p. 271
_____ Using the Grammar Link, TWE p. 271

Reteaching
_____ *Composition Reteaching*, p. 48 *

Enrichment
_____ *Composition Enrichment*, p. 48 *
_____ *Fine Art Transparencies*, 26–30 *

CLOSE
_____ Close activity, TWE p. 271

* Teacher's Classroom Resources

• Homework Assignments •

_____
_____
_____
_____
_____
_____
_____
_____
_____

6.5 Polishing an Argument *SE/TWE pp. 272–275*

Teacher's Name _____ Date _____

Grade _____ Class(es) _____ Date(s)_____ M Tu W Th F

FOCUS
LESSON OVERVIEW
Objective: To draw conclusions about methods of presenting persuasive writing
Skills: evaluating and revising a draft; examining word choices
Critical Thinking: defining; analyzing; drawing conclusions
Speaking and Listening: speaking and listening in class discussions

_____ Bellringer and Grammar Link to the Bellringer, TWE p. 272
_____ Motivating Activity, TWE p. 272

TEACH
Guided Practice
_____ L2, Using the Model, TWE p. 273
_____ L2, Cooperative Learning, TWE p. 273
_____ Two-Minute Skill Drill, TWE p. 273
_____ Journal Writing Tip, TWE p. 273
_____ L2, Using the Model, TWE p. 274
_____ L2, Choosing Precise Words, TWE p. 274
_____ Enabling Strategies: LEP, TWE p. 274

Independent Practice
_____ *Fine Art Transparencies*, 26–30 *
_____ *Writing Process Transparencies*, 20–22B *
_____ *Writing Across the Curriculum*, pp. 10, 21, 24 *
_____ *Cooperative Learning Activities*, pp. 31–36 *
_____ *Thinking and Study Skills*, pp. 14, 25–29 *
_____ *Sentence Combining Practice*, pp. 33–35 *
_____ *Speaking and Listening Activities*, p. 22 *
_____ *Composition Practice*, p. 49 *

• *Homework Assignments* •

_____
_____
_____
_____
_____
_____
_____
_____
_____

ASSESS
_____ Writing Activities Evaluation Guidelines, TWE p. 275
_____ Computer Option, TWE p. 275
_____ Using the Grammar Link, TWE p. 275

Reteaching
_____ *Composition Reteaching*, p. 49 *

Enrichment
_____ *Composition Enrichment*, p. 49 *

CLOSE
_____ Close activity, TWE p. 275

* Teacher's Classroom Resources

6.6 Writing Publicity *SE/TWE pp. 276–279*

Teacher's Name _____ Date _____

Grade _____ Class(es) _____ Date(s)_____ M Tu W Th F

FOCUS

LESSON OVERVIEW

Objective: To evaluate ideas for publicity and to predict audience response in order to write an advertisement

Skills: capturing audience attention; creating visually effective posters

Critical Thinking: analyzing; defining criteria; visualizing; making decisions

Speaking and Listening: speaking and listening in class discussions

_____ Bellringer and Grammar Link to the Bellringer, TWE p. 276

_____ Motivating Activity, TWE p. 276

TEACH

Guided Practice

_____ L2, Cooperative Learning, TWE p. 277

_____ L1, Getting Attention, TWE p. 277

_____ Two-Minute Skill Drill, TWE p. 277

_____ Journal Writing Tip, TWE p. 277

_____ L2, Analyzing Posters, TWE p. 278

_____ L3, Creating an Ad Campaign, TWE p. 278

_____ Enabling Strategies: LEP, TWE p. 278

Independent Practice

_____ *Fine Art Transparencies*, 26–30 *

_____ *Writing Process Transparencies*, 20–22B *

_____ *Writing Across the Curriculum*, pp. 10, 21, 24 *

_____ *Cooperative Learning Activities*, pp. 31–36 *

_____ *Thinking and Study Skills*, pp. 4, 8, 9, 17, 22 *

_____ *Sentence Combining Practice*, pp. 33–35 *

_____ *Speaking and Listening Activities*, p. 22 *

_____ *Composition Practice*, p. 50 *

ASSESS

_____ Writing Activities Evaluation Guidelines, TWE p. 279

_____ Using the Grammar Link, TWE p. 279

Reteaching

_____ *Composition Reteaching*, p. 50 *

Enrichment

_____ *Composition Enrichment*, p. 50 *

_____ *Fine Art Transparencies*, 26–30 *

_____ About the Art, TWE p. 279

CLOSE

_____ Close activity, TWE p. 279

* Teacher's Classroom Resources

• *Homework Assignments* •

_____

_____

_____

_____

_____

_____

_____

_____

6.7 Writing a Letter of Complaint *SE/TWE pp. 280–283*

Teacher's Name _____ Date _____

Grade _____ Class(es) _____ Date(s)_____ M Tu W Th F

FOCUS

LESSON OVERVIEW

Objective: To define and clarify a problem in a letter of complaint
Skills: using correct business letter format; employing appropriate language; explaining a problem and its solution
Critical Thinking: analyzing; defining; making decisions
Speaking and Listening: speaking and listening in class discussions

_____ Bellringer and Grammar Link to the Bellringer, TWE p. 280
_____ Motivating Activity, TWE p. 280

TEACH

• Homework Assignments •

Guided Practice

_____ L2, Using the Model, TWE p. 281
_____ Two-Minute Skill Drill, TWE p. 281
_____ Journal Writing Tip, TWE p. 281
_____ L2, Using the Model, TWE p. 282
_____ L1, Posing Solutions, TWE p. 282
_____ Enabling Strategies: LEP, TWE p. 282

Independent Practice

_____ *Fine Art Transparencies, 26–30 **
_____ *Writing Process Transparencies, 20–22B **
_____ *Writing Across the Curriculum, p. 21 **
_____ *Cooperative Learning Activities, pp. 31–36 **
_____ *Thinking and Study Skills, pp. 1, 4, 13–14, 17 **
_____ *Sentence Combining Practice, pp. 33–35 **
_____ *Speaking and Listening Activities, p. 22 **
_____ *Composition Practice, p. 51 **

ASSESS

_____ Writing Activities Evaluation Guidelines, TWE p. 283
_____ Using the Grammar Link, TWE p. 283

Reteaching

_____ *Composition Reteaching, p. 51 **

Enrichment

_____ *Composition Enrichment, p. 51 **

CLOSE

_____ Close activity, TWE p. 283

* Teacher's Classroom Resources

6.8 Writing a Movie Review *SE/TWE pp. 284–287*

Teacher's Name _____ Date _____
Grade _____ Class(es) _____ Date(s)_____ M Tu W Th F

FOCUS
LESSON OVERVIEW
Objective: To draw conclusions about the effectiveness of a movie review
Skills: evaluating a movie's plot, characters, acting, and visual effects; writing a convincing review
Critical Thinking: recalling analyzing, summarizing, identifying evidence
Speaking and Listening: speaking and listening in class discussions

_____ Bellringer and Grammar Link to the Bellringer, TWE p. 284
_____ Motivating Activity, TWE p. 284

TEACH
Guided Practice
_____ L2, Using the Model, TWE p. 285
_____ L2, Cooperative Learning, TWE p. 285
_____ Two-Minute Skill Drill, TWE p. 285
_____ Journal Writing Tip, TWE p. 285
_____ L2, Using the Model, TWE p. 286
_____ Enabling Strategies: LEP, TWE p. 286

Independent Practice
_____ *Fine Art Transparencies*, 26–30 *
_____ *Writing Process Transparencies*, 20–22B *
_____ *Writing Across the Curriculum*, p. 24 *
_____ *Cooperative Learning Activities*, pp. 31–36 *
_____ *Thinking and Study Skills*, pp. 3, 9, 13, 18–19 *
_____ *Sentence Combining Practice*, pp. 33–35 *
_____ *Speaking and Listening Activities*, p. 22 *
_____ *Composition Practice*, p. 52 *

ASSESS
_____ Writing Activities Evaluation Guidelines, TWE p. 287
_____ Using the Grammar Link, TWE p. 287

Reteaching
_____ *Composition Reteaching*, p. 52 *

Enrichment
_____ *Composition Enrichment*, p. 52 *

CLOSE
_____ Close activity, TWE p. 287

* Teacher's Classroom Resources

```
• Homework Assignments •
_____
_____
_____
_____
_____
_____
_____
_____
```

Unit 6 Writing Process in Action *SE/TWE pp. 288–291*

Teacher's Name _____ Date _____

Grade _____ Class(es) _____ Date(s)_____ M Tu W Th F

FOCUS
LESSON OVERVIEW
Objective: To use persuasive writing techniques in a short persuasive piece
Skills: using the five stages of the writing process: prewriting, drafting, revising, editing, and presenting
Critical Thinking: recalling; synthesizing; defining and clarifying; decision making
Speaking and Listening: note taking; discussing; informal speaking

_____ Bellringer and Grammar Link to the Bellringer, TWE p. 288
_____ Motivating Activity, TWE p. 288

TEACH
Prewriting
_____ L2, Supporting a Topic with Evidence, TWE p. 289

Drafting
_____ L1, Finding a Place to Begin, TWE p. 289

Revising
_____ L2, Peer Editing, TWE p. 290

Editing
_____ L2, Peer Editing, TWE p. 290

Presenting
_____ Presenting activity, TWE p. 290

_____ Journal Writing Tip, TWE p. 290
_____ Enrichment and Extension, TWE p. 290
_____ Speaking and Listening, TWE p. 291

Independent Practice
_____ *Writing Process Transparencies, 20–22B* *
_____ *Thinking and Study Skills, pp. 5, 11, 14–19* *
_____ *Sentence Combining Practice, p. 33–35* *
_____ *Composition Practice, p. 53* *
_____ **Grammar Workbook,** Lessons 69–71

ASSESS
_____ Evaluation Guidelines, TWE p. 291

Reteaching
_____ *Composition Reteaching, p. 53* *

Enrichment
_____ *Composition Enrichment, p. 53* *

CLOSE
_____ Close activity, TWE p. 291

* Teacher's Classroom Resources

• Homework Assignments •

_____
_____
_____
_____
_____
_____
_____
_____

Unit 6 Literature: from "The Liberry," Bel Kaufman *SE/TWE pp. 292–295*

Teacher's Name _____ Date _____
Grade _____ Class(es) _____ Date(s)_____ M Tu W Th F

FOCUS
LESSON OVERVIEW
Objective: To evaluate the effectiveness of an argument in a piece of persuasive writing by a published author
Skills: reading comprehension
Critical Thinking: analyzing; recalling; summarizing
Speaking and Listening: discussing

_____ Bellringer and Motivating Activity, TWE p. 292

TEACH
Guided Practice
_____ L2, Guided Reading, TWE pp. 293–294
_____ Genre and Style, TWE p. 294
_____ Cultural Diversity, TWE p. 295

Independent Practice
_____ *Fine Art Transparencies*, 26–30 *
_____ *Speaking and Listening Activities*, p. 22 *
_____ *Thinking and Study Skills*, pp. 13, 14, 20 *

ASSESS
_____ Evaluation Guidelines for Discussion, TWE p. 295

CLOSE
_____ Close activity, TWE p. 295

* Teacher's Classroom Resources

• Homework Assignments •
_____
_____
_____
_____
_____
_____
_____
_____
_____

UNIT 6 REVIEW *p. 296*
_____ Reflecting on the Unit, TWE p. 296
_____ Writing Across the Curriculum, TWE p. 296
_____ Adding to Your Portfolio, TWE p. 296
_____ Portfolio Evaluation, TWE p. 296

Unit Assessment
_____ *Tests with Answer Key*
Unit 6 Choice A Test, p. 21
Unit 6 Choice B Test, p. 22
Unit 6 Composition Objective
Test, pp. 23–24
_____ *Test Generator*
Unit 6 Choice A Test
Unit 6 Choice B Test
Unit 6 Composition Objective
Test
You may wish to administer one of
these tests as a mastery test.

Unit 7 Troubleshooter SE/TWE pp. 298–320

Teacher's Name _____ Date _____

Grade _____ Class(es) _____ Date(s)_____ M Tu W Th F

LESSON 7.1 *pp. 298–299*

FOCUS
LESSON OVERVIEW
Objective: To recognize a sentence fragment that lacks a subject, a predicate, or both

_____ Bellringer and Motivating Activity, TWE p. 298

TEACH
_____ Cross-reference: Grammar, TWE p. 298
_____ Two-Minute Skill Drill, TWE p. 299

Independent Practice
_____ *Grammar Workbook,* Lesson 5

CLOSE
_____ Close activity, TWE p. 299

LESSON 7.2 *pp. 300–301*

FOCUS
LESSON OVERVIEW
Objective: To recognize the different kinds of run-on sentences

_____ Bellringer and Motivating Activity, TWE p. 300

TEACH
_____ Cross-reference: Grammar, TWE p. 300
_____ Two-Minute Skill Drill, TWE p. 301

Independent Practice
_____ *Grammar Workbook,* Lesson 42

CLOSE
_____ Close activity, TWE p. 301

• *Homework Assignments* •

_____

_____

_____

_____

_____

_____

_____

_____

Unit 7 Troubleshooter SE/TWE pp. 298–320

Teacher's Name _____ Date _____

Grade _____ Class(es) _____ Date(s)_____ M Tu W Th F

LESSON 7.3 *pp. 302–305*

FOCUS
LESSON OVERVIEW
Objective: To avoid common errors in subject-verb agreement associated with various sentence constructions

_____ Bellringer and Motivating Activity, TWE p. 302

TEACH
_____ Cross-reference: Usage, TWE pp. 302–304
_____ Two-Minute Skill Drill, TWE p. 305

Independent Practice
_____ *Sentence Combining Practice*, pp. 16–17 *
_____ ***Grammar Workbook,*** Lesson 54

CLOSE
_____ Close activity, TWE p. 305

┌─────────────────────────────────┐
│ • *Homework Assignments* •   │
│   │
│ _____   │
│ _____   │
│ _____   │
│ _____   │
│ _____   │
│ _____   │
│ _____   │
│ _____   │
│ _____   │
└─────────────────────────────────┘

LESSON 7.4 *pp. 306–307*

FOCUS
LESSON OVERVIEW
Objective: To recognize and correct errors in verb tense or form, such as missing verb endings, improperly formed irregular verbs, and improperly used past and past participle forms

_____ Bellringer and Motivating Activity, TWE p. 306

TEACH
_____ Cross-reference: Grammar, TWE p. 306
_____ Two-Minute Skill Drill, TWE p. 307

Independent Practice
_____ ***Grammar Workbook,*** Lesson 16

CLOSE
_____ Close activity, TWE p. 307

* Teacher's Classroom Resources

Unit 7 Troubleshooter *SE/TWE pp. 298–320*

Teacher's Name _____ Date _____

Grade _____ Class(es) _____ Date(s)_____ M Tu W Th F

LESSON 7.5 *pp. 308–309*

FOCUS
LESSON OVERVIEW
Objective: To recognize the constructions that give rise to incorrect pronoun use

_____ Bellringer and Motivating Activity, TWE p. 308

TEACH
_____ Cross-reference: Grammar, TWE pp. 308–309
_____ Two-Minute Skill Drill, TWE p. 309

Independent Practice
_____ *Grammar Workbook,* Lesson 24

CLOSE
_____ Close activity, TWE p. 309

LESSON 7.6 *pp. 310–311*

FOCUS
LESSON OVERVIEW
Objective: To recognize and correct errors in regular and irregular forms of comparative and superlative adjectives

_____ Bellringer and Motivating Activity, TWE p. 310

TEACH
_____ Cross-reference: Grammar, TWE p. 310
_____ Two-Minute Skill Drill, TWE p. 311

Independent Practice
_____ *Grammar Workbook,* Lesson 30

CLOSE
_____ Close activity, TWE p. 311

> **• Homework Assignments •**
>
> _____
> _____
> _____
> _____
> _____
> _____
> _____
> _____

Unit 7 Troubleshooter *SE/TWE pp. 298–320*

Teacher's Name _____ Date _____

Grade _____ Class(es) _____ Date(s) _____ M Tu W Th F

LESSON 7.7 *pp. 312–313*

FOCUS
LESSON OVERVIEW
Objective: To recognize when commas are needed to separate three or more items in a series, when commas are needed to set off direct quotations, and when commas are needed with nonessential appositives

_____ Bellringer and Motivating Activity, TWE p. 312

TEACH
_____ Cross-reference: Mechanics, TWE pp. 312–313
_____ Two-Minute Skill Drill, TWE p. 313

Independent Practice
_____ *Sentence Combining Practice*, p. 4 *
_____ ***Grammar Workbook,*** Lessons 73–74, 76

CLOSE
_____ Close activity, TWE p. 313

LESSON 7.8 *pp. 314–316*

FOCUS
LESSON OVERVIEW
Objective: To recognize the most common instances in which possessive apostrophes are missing or misplaced and to use possessive apostrophes where appropriate

_____ Bellringer and Motivating Activity, TWE p. 314

TEACH
_____ Cross-reference: Mechanics, TWE pp. 314–315
_____ Cross-reference: Grammar, TWE pp. 315–316
_____ Two-Minute Skill Drill, TWE p. 316

Independent Practice
_____ *Sentence Combining Practice*, p. 9 *
_____ ***Grammar Workbook,*** Lesson 82

CLOSE
_____ Close activity, TWE p. 316

* Teacher's Classroom Resources

> **• Homework Assignments •**
>
> _____
> _____
> _____
> _____
> _____
> _____
> _____
> _____
> _____

Unit 7 Troubleshooter *SE/TWE pp. 298–320*

Teacher's Name _____ Date _____

Grade _____ Class(es) _____ Date(s)_____ M Tu W Th F

LESSON 7.9 *pp. 317–318*

FOCUS
LESSON OVERVIEW
Objective: To avoid or correct errors in capitalization when referring to ethnic groups, nationalities, languages, and family relationships, and when beginning direct quotations

_____ Bellringer and Motivating Activity, TWE p. 317

TEACH
_____ Cross-reference: Mechanics, TWE pp. 317–318
_____ Two-Minute Skill Drill, TWE p. 318

Independent Practice
_____ *Grammar Workbook,* Lessons 68–69, 71

CLOSE
_____ Close activity, TWE p. 318

• *Homework Assignments* •

_____
_____
_____
_____
_____
_____
_____
_____

Unit 8 Subjects, Predicates, and Sentences

SE/TWE pp. 321-342

Teacher's Name _____ Date _____

Grade _____ Class(es) _____ Date(s)_____ M Tu W Th F

LESSON 8.1 *pp. 322–323*

FOCUS
LESSON OVERVIEW
Objective: To identify and use the four kinds of sentences: declarative, interrogative, exclamatory, and imperative

_____ Bellringer and Motivating Activity, TWE p. 322

TEACH
_____ Vocabulary Link, TWE p. 322
_____ Cross-reference: Mechanics, TWE p. 322
_____ Enabling Strategies: LEP, TWE p. 323

PRACTICE AND ASSESS
_____ Answers to Exercises 1 and 2, TWE p. 323

Independent Practice
_____ *Grammar Practice,* p. 1 *
_____ *Grammar Enrichment,* p. 1 *
_____ **Grammar Workbook,** Lessons 1–2

CLOSE
_____ Close activity, TWE p. 323

LESSON 8.2 *pp. 324–325*

FOCUS
LESSON OVERVIEW
Objective: To identify the subject and the predicate of a sentence and to use complete sentences rather than sentence fragments

_____ Bellringer and Motivating Activity, TWE p. 324

TEACH
_____ Teaching Tip, TWE p. 324
_____ Enabling Strategies: LEP, TWE p. 325

PRACTICE AND ASSESS
_____ Answers to Exercises 3 and 4, TWE p. 325

Independent Practice
_____ *Grammar Practice,* p. 1 *
_____ *Grammar Reteaching,* p. 1 *
_____ *Grammar Enrichment,* p. 1 *
_____ **Grammar Workbook,** Lesson 5

Unit Assessment
_____ *Tests with Answer Key*
Unit 8 Pretest, pp. 29–30
_____ *Test Generator*
Unit 8 Pretest
You may wish to administer the Unit 8 Pretest at this point.

• Homework Assignments •

_____
_____
_____
_____
_____
_____
_____
_____
_____

CLOSE
_____ Close activity, TWE p. 325

* Teacher's Classroom Resources

Unit 8 Subjects, Predicates, and Sentences

SE/TWE pp. 321-342

Teacher's Name _____ Date _____

Grade _____ Class(es) _____ Date(s)_____ M Tu W Th F

LESSON 8.3 *pp. 326–327*

FOCUS
LESSON OVERVIEW
Objective: To identify simple and complete subjects and predicates

_____ Bellringer and Motivating Activity, TWE p. 326

TEACH
_____ Grammar Tip, TWE p. 326
_____ Enabling Strategies: LEP, TWE p. 327

PRACTICE AND ASSESS
_____ Answers to Exercises 5 and 6, TWE p. 327

Independent Practice
_____ *Grammar Practice,* p. 2 *
_____ *Grammar Reteaching,* p. 2 *
_____ *Grammar Enrichment,* p. 2 *
_____ **Grammar Workbook,** Lessons 3–4

CLOSE
_____ Close activity, TWE p. 327

LESSON 8.4 *pp. 328–329*

FOCUS
LESSON OVERVIEW
Objective: To use appropriate word order in creating sentences

_____ Bellringer and Motivating Activity, TWE p. 328

TEACH
_____ Grammar Tip, TWE p. 328
_____ Enabling Strategies: LEP, TWE p. 329

PRACTICE AND ASSESS
_____ Answers to Exercises 7 and 8, TWE p. 329

Independent Practice
_____ *Grammar Practice,* p. 3 *
_____ *Grammar Reteaching,* p. 3 *
_____ *Grammar Enrichment,* p. 3 *
_____ **Grammar Workbook,** Lesson 3

• *Homework Assignments* •

_____
_____
_____
_____
_____
_____
_____
_____

CLOSE
_____ Close activity, TWE p. 329

* Teacher's Classroom Resources

Unit 8 Subjects, Predicates, and Sentences

SE/TWE pp. 321-342

Teacher's Name _____ Date _____
Grade _____ Class(es) _____ Date(s)_____ M Tu W Th F

LESSON 8.5 *pp. 330–331*

FOCUS
LESSON OVERVIEW
Objective: To use compound subjects and compound predicates appropriately and to use the correct verb forms with compound subjects

_____ Bellringer and Motivating Activity, TWE p. 330

TEACH
_____ Teaching Tip, TWE p. 330
_____ Enabling Strategies: LEP, TWE p. 331

PRACTICE AND ASSESS
_____ Answers to Exercises 9 and 10, TWE p. 331

Independent Practice
_____ *Grammar Practice*, p. 2 *
_____ *Grammar Reteaching*, p. 4 *
_____ *Grammar Enrichment*, p. 2 *
_____ **Grammar Workbook**, Lesson 4

CLOSE
_____ Close activity, TWE p. 331

LESSON 8.6 *pp. 332–333*

FOCUS
LESSON OVERVIEW
Objective: To use simple sentences and compound sentences appropriately and to avoid or correct run-on sentences

_____ Bellringer and Motivating Activity, TWE p. 332

TEACH
_____ Enabling Strategies: LEP, TWE p. 333

PRACTICE AND ASSESS
_____ Answers to Exercise 11, TWE p. 333

Independent Practice
_____ *Grammar Practice*, p. 4 *
_____ *Grammar Enrichment*, p. 4 *
_____ **Grammar Workbook**, Lesson 6

CLOSE
_____ Close activity, TWE p. 333

* Teacher's Classroom Resources

• Homework Assignments •

_____
_____
_____
_____
_____
_____
_____
_____

Unit 8 Subjects, Predicates, and Sentences

SE/TWE pp. 321-342

Teacher's Name _____ Date _____

Grade _____ Class(es) _____ Date(s)_____ M Tu W Th F

UNIT 8 REVIEW *pp. 334–341*

TEACH
_____ About the Literature, TWE p. 334
_____ Linking Grammar and Literature, TWE p. 334
_____ Teaching Tip, TWE p. 334
_____ About the Art, TWE p. 340

PRACTICE AND ASSESS
_____ Answers to Exercises 1–11, TWE p. 335–341

CLOSE
_____ Close activity, TWE p. 341

Writing Application *p. 342*
_____ Sentence Types in Writing, TWE p. 342
_____ Techniques with Sentence Types, TWE p. 342
_____ Practice, TWE p. 342

Unit Assessment

_____ *Tests with Answer Key*
     Unit 8 Mastery Test, pp. 31–32
_____ *Test Generator*
     Unit 8 Mastery Test
You may wish to administer the Unit 8
Mastery Test at this point.

Unit 9 Nouns *SE/TWE pp. 344–362*

Teacher's Name _____ Date _____

Grade _____ Class(es) _____ Date(s)_____ M Tu W Th F

LESSON 9.1 *pp. 344–345*

FOCUS
LESSON OVERVIEW
Objective: To recognize common, proper, abstract, and concrete nouns

_____ Bellringer, TWE p. 344

TEACH
_____ Teaching Tip, TWE p. 344
_____ Two-Minute Skill Drill, TWE p. 344
_____ Enabling Strategies: LEP, TWE p. 345

PRACTICE AND ASSESS
_____ Answers to Exercises 1 and 2, TWE p. 345

Independent Practice
_____ *Grammar Practice*, p. 5 *
_____ *Grammar Enrichment*, p. 5 *
_____ **Grammar Workbook,** Lesson 7

CLOSE
_____ Close activity, TWE p. 345

LESSON 9.2 *pp. 346–347*

FOCUS
LESSON OVERVIEW
Objective: To identify and correctly pluralize compound nouns

_____ Bellringer and Motivating Activity, TWE p. 346

TEACH
_____ Teaching Tip, TWE p. 346
_____ Enabling Strategies: LEP, TWE p. 347

PRACTICE AND ASSESS
_____ Answers to Exercises 3 and 4, TWE p. 347

Independent Practice
_____ *Grammar Practice*, p. 5 *
_____ *Grammar Reteaching*, p. 5 *
_____ *Grammar Enrichment*, p. 5 *
_____ **Grammar Workbook,** Lesson 9

Unit Assessment

_____ *Tests with Answer Key*
Unit 9 Pretest, pp. 33–34
_____ *Test Generator*
Unit 9 Pretest
You may wish to administer the Unit 9 Pretest at this point.

• *Homework Assignments* •

_____

_____

_____

_____

_____

_____

_____

_____

_____

CLOSE
_____ Close activity, TWE p. 347

* Teacher's Classroom Resources

Unit 9 Nouns *SE/TWE pp. 344–362*

Teacher's Name _____ Date _____

Grade _____ Class(es) _____ Date(s)_____ M Tu W Th F

LESSON 9.3 *pp. 348–349*

FOCUS
LESSON OVERVIEW

Objective: To identify possessive nouns and use them appropriately

_____ Bellringer and Motivating Activity, TWE p. 348

TEACH
_____ Vocabulary Link, TWE p. 348
_____ Grammar Tip, TWE p. 348
_____ Enabling Strategies: LEP, TWE p. 349

PRACTICE AND ASSESS
_____ Answers to Exercises 5 and 6, TWE p. 349

Independent Practice
_____ *Grammar Practice,* p. 6 *
_____ *Grammar Reteaching,* p. 6 *
_____ **Grammar Workbook,** Lesson 9

CLOSE
_____ Close activity, TWE p. 349

LESSON 9.4 *pp. 350–351*

FOCUS
LESSON OVERVIEW

Objective: To use plurals, possessives, and contractions correctly

_____ Bellringer and Motivating Activity, TWE p. 350

TEACH
_____ Enabling Strategies: LEP, TWE p. 351

PRACTICE AND ASSESS
_____ Answers to Exercises 7 and 8, TWE p. 351

Independent Practice
_____ *Grammar Practice,* p. 6 *
_____ *Grammar Reteaching,* p. 7 *
_____ *Grammar Enrichment,* p. 6 *
_____ **Grammar Workbook,** Lesson 10

CLOSE
_____ Close activity, TWE p. 351

* Teacher's Classroom Resources

> **• Homework Assignments •**
>
> _____
> _____
> _____
> _____
> _____
> _____
> _____
> _____

Unit 9 Nouns *SE/TWE pp. 344–362*

Teacher's Name _____ Date _____
Grade _____ Class(es) _____ Date(s)_____ M Tu W Th F

LESSON 9.5 *pp. 352–353*

FOCUS
LESSON OVERVIEW
Objective: To identify and correctly use collective nouns

_____ Bellringer and Motivating Activity, TWE p. 352

TEACH
_____ Cross-reference: Usage, TWE p. 352
_____ Enabling Strategies: LEP, TWE p. 353

PRACTICE AND ASSESS
_____ Answers to Exercises 9 and 10, TWE p. 353

Independent Practice
_____ *Grammar Practice*, p. 5 *
_____ *Grammar Enrichment*, p. 5 *
_____ **Grammar Workbook,** Lesson 8

CLOSE
_____ Close activity, TWE p. 353

LESSON 9.6 *pp. 354–355*

FOCUS
LESSON OVERVIEW
Objective: To use appositives appropriately

_____ Bellringer and Motivating Activity, TWE p. 354

TEACH
_____ Teaching Tip, TWE p. 354
_____ Enabling Strategies: LEP, TWE p. 355

PRACTICE AND ASSESS
_____ Answers to Exercises 11 and 12, TWE p. 355

Independent Practice
_____ *Grammar Practice*, p. 7 *
_____ *Grammar Reteaching*, p. 8 *
_____ *Grammar Enrichment*, p. 7 *
_____ **Grammar Workbook,** Lesson 11

CLOSE
_____ Close activity, TWE p. 355

* Teacher's Classroom Resources

• Homework Assignments •

_____
_____
_____
_____
_____
_____
_____
_____

Unit 9 Nouns *SE/TWE pp. 344–362*

Teacher's Name _____ Date _____

Grade _____ Class(es) _____ Date(s)_____ M Tu W Th F

UNIT 9 REVIEW *pp. 356–361*

TEACH
_____ About the Literature, TWE p. 356
_____ Linking Grammar and Literature, TWE p. 356
_____ Grammar Tip, TWE p. 356
_____ About the Art, TWE p. 360

PRACTICE AND ASSESS
_____ Answers to Exercises 1–7, TWE pp. 357–361

CLOSE
_____ Close activity, TWE p. 361

Writing Application *p. 362*
_____ Nouns in Writing, TWE p. 362
_____ Techniques with Nouns, TWE p. 362
_____ Practice, TWE p. 362

Unit Assessment
_____ *Tests with Answer Key*   Unit 9 Mastery Test, pp. 35–36   _____ *Test Generator*   Unit 9 Mastery Test   You may wish to administer the Unit 9 Mastery Test at this point.

Unit 10 Verbs *SE/TWE pp. 364–392*

Teacher's Name _____ Date _____

Grade _____ Class(es) _____ Date(s)_____ M Tu W Th F

LESSON 10.1 *pp. 364–365*

FOCUS
LESSON OVERVIEW
Objective: To identify and select appropriate action verbs and to distinguish between action verbs that express physical action and those that express mental activities

_____ Bellringer and Motivating Activity, TWE p. 364

TEACH
_____ Teaching Tip, TWE p. 364
_____ Enabling Strategies: LEP, TWE p. 365

PRACTICE AND ASSESS
_____ Answers to Exercises 1 and 2, TWE p. 365

Independent Practice
_____ *Grammar Reteaching*, p. 9 *
_____ ***Grammar Workbook,*** Lesson 12

CLOSE
_____ Close activity, TWE p. 365

LESSON 10.2 *pp. 366–367*

FOCUS
LESSON OVERVIEW
Objective: To use transitive and intransitive verbs and direct objects appropriately

_____ Bellringer and Motivating Activity, TWE p. 366

TEACH
_____ Grammar Tip, TWE p. 366
_____ Cross-reference: Dictionary, TWE p. 366
_____ Enabling Strategies: LEP, TWE p. 367

PRACTICE AND ASSESS
_____ Answers to Exercises 3 and 4, TWE p. 367

Independent Practice
_____ *Grammar Practice*, p. 8 *
_____ *Grammar Reteaching*, p. 10 *
_____ *Grammar Enrichment*, p. 8 *
_____ ***Grammar Workbook,*** Lesson 13

Unit Assessment

_____ *Tests with Answer Key*
     Unit 10 Pretest, pp. 37–38
_____ *Test Generator*
     Unit 10 Pretest
You may wish to administer the Unit 10 Pretest at this point.

• *Homework Assignments* •

_____

_____

_____

_____

_____

_____

_____

_____

CLOSE
_____ Close activity, TWE p. 367

* Teacher's Classroom Resources

Unit 10 Verbs *SE/TWE pp. 364–392*

Teacher's Name _____ Date _____

Grade _____ Class(es) _____ Date(s) _____ M Tu W Th F

LESSON 10.3 *pp. 368–369*

FOCUS
LESSON OVERVIEW
Objective: To distinguish between direct objects and indirect objects

_____ Bellringer and Motivating Activity, TWE p. 368

TEACH
_____ Grammar Tip, TWE p. 368
_____ Enabling Strategies: LEP, TWE p. 369

PRACTICE AND ASSESS
_____ Answers to Exercises 5 and 6, TWE p. 369

Independent Practice
_____ *Grammar Practice,* p. 9 *
_____ *Grammar Reteaching,* p. 11 *
_____ *Grammar Enrichment,* p. 9 *
_____ **Grammar Workbook,** Lesson 14

CLOSE
_____ Close activity, TWE p. 369

LESSON 10.4 *pp. 370–371*

FOCUS
LESSON OVERVIEW
Objective: To distinguish between action verbs and linking verbs and to identify predicate nouns and predicate adjectives

_____ Bellringer and Motivating Activity, TWE p. 370

TEACH
_____ Enabling Strategies: LEP, TWE p. 371

PRACTICE AND ASSESS
_____ Answers to Exercises 7 and 8, TWE p. 371

Independent Practice
_____ *Grammar Practice,* p. 10 *
_____ *Grammar Reteaching,* p. 12 *
_____ *Grammar Enrichment,* p. 10 *
_____ **Grammar Workbook,** Lesson 15

• Homework Assignments •

_____
_____
_____
_____
_____
_____
_____
_____

CLOSE
_____ Close activity, TWE p. 371

* Teacher's Classroom Resources

Unit 10 Verbs *SE/TWE pp. 364–392*

Teacher's Name _____ Date _____

Grade _____ Class(es) _____ Date(s)_____ M Tu W Th F

LESSON 10.5 *pp. 372–373*

FOCUS
LESSON OVERVIEW
Objective: To distinguish between the present, past, and future verb tenses and to use these tenses appropriately

_____ Bellringer and Motivating Activity, TWE p. 372

TEACH
_____ Vocabulary Link, TWE p. 372
_____ Enabling Strategies: LEP, TWE p. 373
_____ Enabling Strategies: L3, TWE p. 373

PRACTICE AND ASSESS
_____ Answers to Exercises 9 and 10, TWE p. 373

Independent Practice
_____ *Grammar Practice*, p.11 *
_____ *Grammar Reteaching*, p. 13 *
_____ *Grammar Enrichment*, p. 11 *
_____ **Grammar Workbook,** Lesson 16

CLOSE
_____ Close activity, TWE p. 373

LESSON 10.6 *pp. 374–375*

FOCUS
LESSON OVERVIEW
Objective: To distinguish between main verbs and helping verbs and to identify the present participle and past participle in main verbs

_____ Bellringer and Motivating Activity, TWE p. 374

TEACH
_____ Cross-reference: Grammar, TWE p. 374
_____ Enabling Strategies: LEP, TWE p. 375

PRACTICE AND ASSESS
_____ Answers to Exercise 11, TWE p. 375

Independent Practice
_____ *Grammar Practice*, p. 12 *
_____ *Grammar Reteaching*, p. 14 *
_____ *Grammar Enrichment*, p. 12 *
_____ **Grammar Workbook,** Lesson 17

• *Homework Assignments* •

_____
_____
_____
_____
_____
_____
_____
_____

CLOSE
_____ Close activity, TWE p. 375

* Teacher's Classroom Resources

Unit 10 Verbs *SE/TWE pp. 364–392*

Teacher's Name _____ Date _____

Grade _____ Class(es) _____ Date(s)_____ M Tu W Th F

LESSON 10.7 *pp. 376–377*

FOCUS
LESSON OVERVIEW
Objective: To identify and use the present and past progressive forms appropriately

_____ Bellringer and Motivating Activity, TWE p. 376

TEACH
_____ Vocabulary Link, TWE p. 376
_____ Enabling Strategies: LEP, TWE p. 377

PRACTICE AND ASSESS
_____ Answers to Exercises 12 and 13, TWE p. 377

Independent Practice
_____ *Grammar Practice*, p. 13 *
_____ *Grammar Enrichment*, p. 9 *
_____ **Grammar Workbook,** Lesson 18

CLOSE
_____ Close activity, TWE p. 377

LESSON 10.8 *pp. 378–379*

FOCUS
LESSON OVERVIEW
Objective: To identify and use present perfect and past perfect tenses

_____ Bellringer and Motivating Activity, TWE p. 378

TEACH
_____ Teaching Tip, TWE p. 378
_____ Cross-reference: Spelling, TWE p. 378
_____ Enabling Strategies: LEP, TWE p. 379

PRACTICE AND ASSESS
_____ Answers to Exercises 14 and 15, TWE p. 379

Independent Practice
_____ *Grammar Practice*, p. 13 *
_____ *Grammar Reteaching*, p. 15 *
_____ *Grammar Enrichment*, p. 13 *
_____ **Grammar Workbook,** Lesson 19

CLOSE
_____ Close activity, TWE p. 379

* Teacher's Classroom Resources

• Homework Assignments •

_____
_____
_____
_____
_____
_____
_____
_____
_____

Unit 10 Verbs *SE/TWE pp. 364–392*

Teacher's Name _____ Date _____

Grade _____ Class(es) _____ Date(s) _____ M Tu W Th F

LESSON 10.9 *pp. 380–381*

FOCUS
LESSON OVERVIEW
Objective: To use the past tense and past participle of irregular verbs appropriately

_____ Bellringer, TWE p. 380

TEACH
_____ Teaching Tip, TWE p. 380
_____ Cross-reference: Dictionary, TWE p. 380
_____ Two-Minute Skill Drill, TWE p. 381
_____ Enabling Strategies: LEP, TWE p. 381

PRACTICE AND ASSESS
_____ Answers to Exercise 16, TWE p. 381

Independent Practice
_____ *Grammar Practice*, p. 14 *
_____ *Grammar Reteaching*, p. 16 *
_____ *Grammar Enrichment*, p. 14 *
_____ **Grammar Workbook,** Lesson 20

CLOSE
_____ Close activity, TWE p. 381

LESSON 10.10 *pp. 382–383*

FOCUS
LESSON OVERVIEW
Objective: To use the correct past tense and past participle form of irregular verbs

_____ Bellringer and Motivating Activity, TWE p. 382

TEACH
_____ Enabling Strategies: LEP, TWE p. 383

PRACTICE AND ASSESS
_____ Answers to Exercises 17 and 18, TWE p. 383

Independent Practice
_____ *Grammar Practice*, p. 14 *
_____ *Grammar Reteaching*, p. 16 *
_____ *Grammar Enrichment*, p. 14 *
_____ **Grammar Workbook,** Lessons 20–21

• Homework Assignments •

_____
_____
_____
_____
_____
_____
_____
_____

CLOSE
_____ Close activity, TWE p. 383

* Teacher's Classroom Resources

Unit 10 Verbs *SE/TWE pp. 364–392*

Teacher's Name _____ Date _____

Grade _____ Class(es) _____ Date(s)_____ M Tu W Th F

UNIT 10 REVIEW *pp. 384–391*

TEACH

_____ About the Literature, TWE p. 384
_____ Linking Grammar and Literature, TWE p. 384
_____ Teaching Tip, TWE p. 384
_____ About the Art, TWE p. 391

PRACTICE AND ASSESS

_____ Answers to Exercises 1–12, TWE p. 385–390

CLOSE

_____ Close activity, TWE p. 391

Writing Application *p. 392*

_____ Verbs in Writing, TWE p. 392
_____ Techniques with Verbs, TWE p. 392
_____ Practice, TWE p. 392

> ### Unit Assessment
>
> _____ *Tests with Answer Key*
>   Unit 10 Mastery Test, pp. 39–40
> _____ *Test Generator*
>   Unit 10 Mastery Test
> You may wish to administer the
> Unit 10 Mastery Test at this point.

Unit 11 Pronouns SE/TWE pp. 393–414

Teacher's Name _____ Date _____

Grade _____ Class(es) _____ Date(s)_____ M Tu W Th F

LESSON 11.1 *pp. 394–395*

FOCUS
LESSON OVERVIEW
Objective: To correctly identify and use personal pronouns as subjects and objects in sentences

_____ Bellringer and Motivating Activity, TWE p. 394

TEACH
_____ Teaching Tip, TWE p. 394
_____ Enabling Strategies: LEP, TWE p. 395

PRACTICE AND ASSESS
_____ Answers to Exercises 1 and 2, TWE p. 395

Independent Practice
_____ *Grammar Practice,* p. 15 *
_____ *Grammar Reteaching,* p. 17 *
_____ *Grammar Enrichment,* p. 15 *
_____ **Grammar Workbook,** Lesson 22

CLOSE
_____ Close activity, TWE p. 395

LESSON 11.2 *pp. 396–397*

FOCUS
LESSON OVERVIEW
Objective: To make pronouns agree clearly and correctly with their antecedents

_____ Bellringer and Motivating Activity, TWE p. 396

TEACH
_____ Teaching Tip, TWE p. 396
_____ Cross-reference: Writing, TWE p. 396
_____ Enabling Strategies: LEP, TWE p. 397

PRACTICE AND ASSESS
_____ Answers to Exercise 3, TWE p. 397

Independent Practice
_____ *Grammar Practice,* p. 16 *
_____ *Grammar Reteaching,* p. 18 *
_____ *Grammar Enrichment,* p. 16 *
_____ **Grammar Workbook,** Lesson 24

Unit Assessment
_____ *Tests with Answer Key* Unit 11 Pretest, pp. 41–42
_____ *Test Generator* Unit 11 Pretest
You may wish to administer the Unit 11 Pretest at this point.

• *Homework Assignments* •
_____
_____
_____
_____
_____
_____
_____
_____
_____

CLOSE
_____ Close activity, TWE p. 397

* Teacher's Classroom Resources

Unit 11 Pronouns *SE/TWE pp. 393–414*

Teacher's Name _____ Date _____

Grade _____ Class(es) _____ Date(s)_____ M Tu W Th F

LESSON 11.3 *pp.398–399*

FOCUS
LESSON OVERVIEW

Objective: To identify and use subject and object pronouns correctly in compound subjects and objects

_____ Bellringer and Motivating Activity, TWE p. 398

TEACH
_____ Grammar Tip, TWE p. 398
_____ Enabling Strategies: LEP, TWE p. 399

PRACTICE AND ASSESS
_____ Answers to Exercises 4 and 5, TWE p. 399

Independent Practice
_____ *Grammar Reteaching,* p. 19 *
_____ **Grammar Workbook,** Lesson 24

CLOSE
_____ Close activity, TWE p. 399

LESSON 11.4 *pp. 400–401*

FOCUS
LESSON OVERVIEW

Objective: To recognize and use possessive pronouns correctly in their singular and plural forms

_____ Bellringer and Motivating Activity, TWE p. 400

TEACH
_____ Cross-reference: Usage, TWE p. 400
_____ Grammar Tip, TWE p. 400
_____ Two-Minute Skill Drill, TWE p. 400
_____ Enabling Strategies: LEP, TWE p. 401

PRACTICE AND ASSESS
_____ Answers to Exercises 6 and 7, TWE p. 401

Independent Practice
_____ *Grammar Practice,* p. 17 *
_____ *Grammar Reteaching,* p. 20 *
_____ *Grammar Enrichment,* p. 17 *
_____ **Grammar Workbook,** Lesson 25

• *Homework Assignments* •

_____
_____
_____
_____
_____
_____
_____
_____

CLOSE
_____ Close activity, TWE p. 401

* Teacher's Classroom Resources

Unit 11 Pronouns *SE/TWE pp. 393–414*

Teacher's Name _____ Date _____

Grade _____ Class(es) _____ Date(s)_____ M Tu W Th F

LESSON 11.5 *pp. 402–403*

FOCUS
LESSON OVERVIEW
Objective: To use indefinite pronouns that agree in number with their verbs and any related pronouns

_____ Bellringer and Motivating Activity, TWE p. 402

TEACH
_____ Grammar Tip, TWE p. 402
_____ Enabling Strategies: LEP, TWE p. 403

PRACTICE AND ASSESS
_____ Answers to Exercises 8 and 9, TWE p. 403

Independent Practice
_____ *Grammar Practice*, p. 18 *
_____ *Grammar Reteaching*, p. 21 *
_____ *Grammar Enrichment*, p.18 *
_____ **Grammar Workbook**, Lesson 25

CLOSE
_____ Close activity, TWE p. 403

LESSON 11.6 *pp. 404–405*

FOCUS
LESSON OVERVIEW
Objective: To identify and differentiate between reflexive and intensive pronouns

_____ Bellringer and Motivating Activity, TWE p. 404

TEACH
_____ Teaching Tip, TWE p. 404
_____ Enabling Strategies: LEP, TWE p. 405

PRACTICE AND ASSESS
_____ Answers to Exercises 10 and 11, TWE p. 405

Independent Practice
_____ *Grammar Practice*, p. 16 *
_____ *Grammar Enrichment*, p. 19 *
_____ **Grammar Workbook**, Lesson 26

CLOSE
_____ Close activity, TWE p. 405

* Teacher's Classroom Resources

• Homework Assignments •

_____
_____
_____
_____
_____
_____
_____
_____

Unit 11 Pronouns *SE/TWE pp. 393–414*

Teacher's Name _____ Date _____
Grade _____ Class(es) _____ Date(s)_____ M Tu W Th F

LESSON 11.7 *pp. 406–407*

FOCUS
LESSON OVERVIEW
Objective: To identify and correctly use interrogative pronouns

_____ Bellringer and Motivating Activity, TWE p. 406

TEACH
_____ Cross-reference: Grammar, TWE p. 406
_____ Enabling Strategies: LEP, TWE p. 407

PRACTICE AND ASSESS
_____ Answers to Exercises 12 and 13, TWE p. 407

Independent Practice
_____ *Grammar Practice*, p. 19 *
_____ *Grammar Reteaching*, p. 22 *
_____ *Grammar Enrichment*, p. 19 *
_____ **Grammar Workbook**, Lesson 27

CLOSE
_____ Close activity, TWE p. 407

* Teacher's Classroom Resources

• **Homework Assignments** •

_____
_____
_____
_____
_____
_____
_____
_____
_____

UNIT 11 REVIEW *pp. 408–413*

TEACH
_____ About the Literature, TWE p. 408
_____ Linking Grammar and Literature, TWE p. 408
_____ About the Art, TWE p. 412

PRACTICE AND ASSESS
_____ Answers to Exercises 1–8, TWE p. 409–413

CLOSE
_____ Close activity, TWE p. 413

Writing Application *p. 414*
_____ Pronouns in Writing, TWE p. 414
_____ Techniques with Pronouns, TWE p. 414
_____ Practice, TWE p. 414

Unit Assessment
_____ *Tests with Answer Key*
Unit 11 Mastery Test, pp. 43–44
_____ *Test Generator*
Unit 11 Mastery Test
You may wish to administer the
Unit 11 Mastery Test at this point.

Unit 12 Adjectives and Adverbs *SE/TWE pp. 415–442*

Teacher's Name _____ Date _____

Grade _____ Class(es) _____ Date(s)_____ M Tu W Th F

LESSON 12.1 *pp. 416–417*

FOCUS
LESSON OVERVIEW
Objective: To identify predicate adjectives and adjectives that precede nouns

_____ Bellringer and Motivating Activity, TWE p. 416

TEACH
_____ Teaching Tip, TWE p. 416
_____ Cross-reference: Grammar, TWE p. 416
_____ Enabling Strategies: LEP, TWE p. 417

PRACTICE AND ASSESS
_____ Answers to Exercises 1 and 2, TWE p. 417

Independent Practice
_____ *Grammar Practice,* p. 20 *
_____ *Grammar Reteaching,* p. 23 *
_____ *Grammar Enrichment,* p. 20 *
_____ ***Grammar Workbook,*** Lesson 28

CLOSE
_____ Close activity, TWE p. 417

LESSON 12.2 *pp. 418–419*

FOCUS
LESSON OVERVIEW
Objective: To recognize appropriate use of definite and indefinite articles and to identify proper adjectives

_____ Bellringer and Motivating Activity, TWE p. 418

TEACH
_____ Grammar Tip, TWE p. 418
_____ Cross-reference: Mechanics, TWE p. 418
_____ Enabling Strategies: LEP, TWE p. 419

PRACTICE AND ASSESS
_____ Answers to Exercises 3, 4, 5, TWE p. 419

Independent Practice
_____ *Grammar Practice,* p. 20 *
_____ *Grammar Reteaching,* p. 24 *
_____ *Grammar Enrichment,* p. 20 *
_____ ***Grammar Workbook,*** Lesson 29

Unit Assessment
_____ *Tests with Answer Key*
    Unit 12 Pretest, pp. 45–46
_____ *Test Generator*
    Unit 12 Pretest
You may wish to administer the
Unit 12 Pretest at this point.

• Homework Assignments •

_____

_____

_____

_____

_____

_____

_____

_____

CLOSE
_____ Close activity, TWE p. 419

* Teacher's Classroom Resources

Unit 12 Adjectives and Adverbs *SE/TWE pp. 415–442*

Teacher's Name _____ Date _____

Grade _____ Class(es) _____ Date(s)_____ M Tu W Th F

LESSON 12.3 *pp. 420–421*

FOCUS
LESSON OVERVIEW
Objective: To recognize and use comparative and superlative adjectives

_____ Bellringer and Motivating Activity, TWE p. 420

TEACH
_____ Grammar Tip, TWE p. 420
_____ Two-Minute Skill Drill, TWE p. 421
_____ Enabling Strategies: LEP, TWE p. 421

PRACTICE AND ASSESS
_____ Answers to Exercise 6, TWE p. 421

Independent Practice
_____ *Grammar Practice*, p. 21 *
_____ *Grammar Reteaching*, p. 24 *
_____ *Grammar Enrichment*, p. 21 *
_____ **Grammar Workbook**, Lesson 30

CLOSE
_____ Close activity, TWE p. 421

LESSON 12.4 *pp. 422–423*

FOCUS
LESSON OVERVIEW
Objective: To identify adjectives that have irregular comparative and superlative forms

_____ Bellringer and Motivating Activity, TWE p. 422

TEACH
_____ Grammar Tip, TWE p. 422
_____ Two-Minute Skill Drill, TWE p. 423
_____ Enabling Strategies: LEP, TWE p. 423
_____ Enabling Strategies: L3, TWE p. 423

PRACTICE AND ASSESS
_____ Answers to Exercises 7 and 8, TWE p. 423

Independent Practice
_____ *Grammar Practice*, p. 21 *
_____ *Grammar Reteaching*, p. 24 *
_____ *Grammar Enrichment*, p. 21 *
_____ **Grammar Workbook**, Lesson 31

CLOSE
_____ Close activity, TWE p. 423

* Teacher's Classroom Resources

> **• Homework Assignments •**
>
> _____
> _____
> _____
> _____
> _____
> _____
> _____
> _____

Unit 12 Adjectives and Adverbs *SE/TWE pp. 415–442*

Teacher's Name _____ Date _____

Grade _____ Class(es) _____ Date(s)_____ M Tu W Th F

LESSON 12.5 *pp. 424–425*

FOCUS
LESSON OVERVIEW
Objective: To identify demonstratives and to determine whether they are used as adjectives or pronouns

_____ Bellringer and Motivating Activity, TWE p. 424

TEACH
_____ Teaching Tip, TWE p. 424
_____ Enabling Strategies: LEP, TWE p. 425

PRACTICE AND ASSESS
_____ Answers to Exercises 9 and 10, TWE p. 425

Independent Practice
_____ *Grammar Practice*, p. 22 *
_____ *Grammar Reteaching*, p. 25 *
_____ *Grammar Enrichment*, p. 22 *
_____ **Grammar Workbook,** Lesson 32

CLOSE
_____ Close activity, TWE p. 425

LESSON 12.6 *pp. 426–427*

FOCUS
LESSON OVERVIEW
Objective: To identify adverbs and the words that they modify

_____ Bellringer and Motivating Activity, TWE p. 426

TEACH
_____ Enabling Strategies: LEP, TWE p. 427

PRACTICE AND ASSESS
_____ Answers to Exercises 11 and 12, TWE p. 427

Independent Practice
_____ *Grammar Practice*, p. 23 *
_____ *Grammar Reteaching*, p. 26 *
_____ *Grammar Enrichment*, p. 23 *
_____ **Grammar Workbook,** Lesson 33

CLOSE
_____ Close activity, TWE p. 427

* Teacher's Classroom Resources

> ### • Homework Assignments •
> _____
> _____
> _____
> _____
> _____
> _____
> _____
> _____

Unit 12 Adjectives and Adverbs *SE/TWE pp. 415–442*

Teacher's Name _____ Date _____

Grade _____ Class(es) _____ Date(s) _____ M Tu W Th F

LESSON 12.7 *pp. 428–429*

FOCUS
LESSON OVERVIEW
Objective: To identify and use intensifiers

_____ Bellringer and Motivating Activity, TWE p. 428

TEACH
_____ Grammar Tip, TWE p. 428
_____ Enabling Strategies: LEP, TWE p. 429

PRACTICE AND ASSESS
_____ Answers to Exercises 13 and 14, TWE p. 429

Independent Practice
_____ *Grammar Practice*, p. 23 *
_____ *Grammar Reteaching*, p. 26 *
_____ *Grammar Enrichment*, p. 24 *
_____ ***Grammar Workbook***, Lesson 34

CLOSE
_____ Close activity, TWE p. 429

LESSON 12.8 *pp. 430–431*

FOCUS
LESSON OVERVIEW
Objective: To identify and use comparative and superlative adverbs

_____ Bellringer and Motivating Activity, TWE p. 430

TEACH
_____ Teaching Tip, TWE p. 430
_____ Two-Minute Skill Drill, TWE p. 431
_____ Enabling Strategies: LEP, TWE p. 431

PRACTICE AND ASSESS
_____ Answers to Exercise 15, TWE p. 431

Independent Practice
_____ ***Grammar Workbook***, Lesson 35

CLOSE
_____ Close activity, TWE p. 431

* Teacher's Classroom Resources

• Homework Assignments •

_____

_____

_____

_____

_____

_____

_____

_____

Unit 12 Adjectives and Adverbs SE/TWE pp. 415–442

Teacher's Name _____ Date _____

Grade _____ Class(es) _____ Date(s)_____ M Tu W Th F

LESSON 12.9 pp. 432–433

FOCUS
LESSON OVERVIEW
Objective: To distinguish between adverbs that follow verbs and predicate adjectives

_____ Bellringer and Motivating Activity, TWE p. 432

TEACH
_____ Teaching Tip, TWE p. 432
_____ Enabling Strategies: LEP, TWE p. 433

PRACTICE AND ASSESS
_____ Answers to Exercises 16 and 17, TWE p. 433

Independent Practice
_____ *Grammar Practice*, p. 25 *
_____ *Grammar Reteaching*, p. 27 *
_____ *Grammar Enrichment*, p. 25 *
_____ ***Grammar Workbook,*** Lesson 36

CLOSE
_____ Close activity, TWE p. 433

LESSON 12.10 pp. 434–435

FOCUS
LESSON OVERVIEW
Objective: To identify and use negative words correctly and to avoid double negatives

_____ Bellringer and Motivating Activity, TWE p. 434

TEACH
_____ Enabling Strategies: LEP, TWE p. 435
_____ Enabling Strategies: L1, TWE p. 435

PRACTICE AND ASSESS
_____ Answers to Exercises 18 and 19, TWE p. 435

Independent Practice
_____ *Grammar Practice*, p. 26 *
_____ *Grammar Reteaching*, p. 28 *
_____ *Grammar Enrichment*, p. 26 *
_____ ***Grammar Workbook,*** Lesson 37

CLOSE
_____ Close activity, TWE p. 435

* Teacher's Classroom Resources

• Homework Assignments •

_____
_____
_____
_____
_____
_____
_____
_____

Unit 12 Adjectives and Adverbs *SE/TWE pp. 415–442*

Teacher's Name _____ Date _____

Grade _____ Class(es) _____ Date(s)_____ M Tu W Th F

UNIT 12 REVIEW *pp. 436–441*

TEACH
_____ About the Literature, TWE p. 436
_____ Linking Grammar and Literature, TWE p. 436
_____ Teaching Tip, TWE p. 436
_____ About the Art, TWE p. 440

PRACTICE AND ASSESS
_____ Answers to Exercises 1–8, TWE p. 437–441

CLOSE
_____ Close activity, TWE p. 441

Writing Application *p. 442*
_____ Adjectives in Writing, TWE p. 442
_____ Techniques with Adjectives, TWE p. 442
_____ Practice, TWE p. 442

> ## Unit Assessment
>
> _____ *Tests with Answer Key*
> Unit 12 Mastery Test, pp. 47–48
> _____ *Test Generator*
> Unit 12 Mastery Test
> You may wish to administer the
> Unit 12 Mastery Test at this point.

Unit 13 Prepositions, Conjunctions, and Interjections *SE/TWE pp. 443–464*

Teacher's Name _____ Date _____

Grade _____ Class(es) _____ Date(s)_____ M Tu W Th F

LESSON 13.1 *pp. 444–445*

FOCUS
LESSON OVERVIEW
Objective: To identify prepositions, prepositional phrases, and objects of prepositions

_____ Bellringer and Motivating Activity, TWE p. 444

TEACH
_____ Teaching Tip, TWE p. 444
_____ Two-Minute Skill Drill, TWE p. 445
_____ Enabling Strategies: LEP, TWE p. 445

PRACTICE AND ASSESS
_____ Answers to Exercise 1, TWE p. 445

Independent Practice
_____ *Grammar Practice*, p. 27 *
_____ *Grammar Reteaching*, p. 29 *
_____ *Grammar Enrichment*, p. 27 *
_____ **Grammar Workbook**, Lesson 38

CLOSE
_____ Close activity, TWE p. 445

LESSON 13.2 *pp. 446–447*

FOCUS
LESSON OVERVIEW
Objective: To identify the correct object pronoun to use after a preposition

_____ Bellringer, TWE p. 446

TEACH
_____ Two-Minute Skill Drill, TWE p. 447
_____ Enabling Strategies: LEP, TWE p. 447

PRACTICE AND ASSESS
_____ Answers to Exercise 2, TWE p. 447

Independent Practice
_____ *Grammar Practice*, p. 28 *
_____ *Grammar Enrichment*, p. 28 *
_____ **Grammar Workbook**, Lesson 39

• Homework Assignments •
_____
_____
_____
_____
_____
_____
_____
_____

CLOSE
_____ Close activity, TWE p. 447

* Teacher's Classroom Resources

Unit 13 Prepositions, Conjunctions, and Interjections *SE/TWE pp. 443–464*

Teacher's Name _____ Date _____

Grade _____ Class(es) _____ Date(s)_____ M Tu W Th F

LESSON 13.3 *pp. 448–449*

FOCUS
LESSON OVERVIEW
Objective: To identify and use prepositional phrases that function as adjectives or adverbs

_____ Bellringer and Motivating Activity, TWE p. 448

TEACH
_____ Teaching Tip, TWE p. 448
_____ Enabling Strategies: LEP, TWE p. 449

PRACTICE AND ASSESS
_____ Answers to Exercise 3, TWE p. 449

Independent Practice
_____ *Grammar Practice,* p. 29 *
_____ *Grammar Enrichment,* p. 29 *
_____ **Grammar Workbook,** Lesson 40

CLOSE
_____ Close activity, TWE p. 449

LESSON 13.4 *pp. 450–451*

FOCUS
LESSON OVERVIEW
Objective: To identify, distinguish between, and use coordinating and correlative conjunctions

_____ Bellringer and Motivating Activity, TWE p. 450

TEACH
_____ Enabling Strategies: LEP, TWE p. 451

PRACTICE AND ASSESS
_____ Answers to Exercises 4 and 5, TWE p. 451

Independent Practice
_____ *Grammar Practice,* p. 30 *
_____ *Grammar Reteaching,* p. 30 *
_____ *Grammar Enrichment,* p. 30 *
_____ **Grammar Workbook,** Lesson 41

CLOSE
_____ Close activity, TWE p. 451

* Teacher's Classroom Resources

• Homework Assignments •

_____
_____
_____
_____
_____
_____
_____
_____
_____

Unit 13 Prepositions, Conjunctions, and Interjections *SE/TWE pp. 443–464*

Teacher's Name _____ Date _____

Grade _____ Class(es) _____ Date(s)_____ M Tu W Th F

LESSON 13.5 *pp. 452–453*

FOCUS
LESSON OVERVIEW
Objective: To identify and correctly punctuate interjections

_____ Bellringer and Motivating Activity, TWE p. 452

TEACH
_____ Grammar Tip, TWE p. 452
_____ Two-Minute Skill Drill, TWE p. 453
_____ Enabling Strategies: LEP, TWE p. 453

PRACTICE AND ASSESS
_____ Answers to Exercises 6 and 7, TWE p. 453

Independent Practice
_____ *Grammar Practice*, p. 30 *
_____ *Grammar Reteaching*, p. 30 *
_____ *Grammar Enrichment*, p. 30 *
_____ **Grammar Workbook**, Lesson 41

CLOSE
_____ Close activity, TWE p. 453

LESSON 13.6 *pp. 454–455*

FOCUS
LESSON OVERVIEW
Objective: To identify the part of speech of every word in a sentence

_____ Bellringer and Motivating Activity, TWE p. 454

TEACH
_____ Cross-reference: Grammar, TWE p. 454
_____ Enabling Strategies: LEP, TWE p. 455

PRACTICE AND ASSESS
_____ Answers to Exercises 8 and 9, TWE p. 455

Independent Practice
_____ *Grammar Reteaching*, p. 31 *
_____ **Grammar Workbook**, Units 2–6

CLOSE
_____ Close activity, TWE p. 455

* Teacher's Classroom Resources

• Homework Assignments •

_____
_____
_____
_____
_____
_____
_____
_____
_____
_____

Unit 13 Prepositions, Conjunctions, and Interjections *SE/TWE pp. 443–464*

Teacher's Name _____ Date _____

Grade _____ Class(es) _____ Date(s)_____ M Tu W Th F

UNIT 13 REVIEW *pp. 456–463*

TEACH

_____ About the Literature, TWE p. 456

_____ Linking Grammar and Literature, TWE p. 456

_____ About the Art, TWE p. 462

PRACTICE AND ASSESS

_____ Answers to Exercises 1–10, TWE p. 457–463

CLOSE

_____ Close activity, TWE p. 463

Writing Application *p. 464*

_____ Prepositions in Writing, TWE p. 464

_____ Techniques with Prepositions, TWE p. 464

_____ Practice, TWE p. 464

Unit Assessment
_____ *Tests with Answer Key* Unit 13 Mastery Test, pp. 51–52 _____ *Test Generator* Unit 13 Mastery Test You may wish to administer the Unit 13 Mastery Test at this point.

Unit 14 Clauses and Complex Sentences *SE/TWE pp. 465–484*

Teacher's Name _____ Date _____

Grade _____ Class(es) _____ Date(s)_____ M Tu W Th F

LESSON 14.1 *pp. 466–467*

FOCUS
LESSON OVERVIEW
Objective: To use main clauses appropriately in simple and compound sentences

_____ Bellringer and Motivating Activity, TWE p. 466

TEACH
_____ Teaching Tip, TWE p. 466
_____ Enabling Strategies: LEP, TWE p. 467

PRACTICE AND ASSESS
_____ Answers to Exercises 1 and 2, TWE p. 467

Independent Practice
_____ *Grammar Practice*, p. 31 *
_____ *Grammar Reteaching*, p. 32 *
_____ *Grammar Enrichment*, p. 31 *
_____ **Grammar Workbook,** Lesson 42

CLOSE
_____ Close activity, TWE p. 467

LESSON 14.2 *pp. 468–469*

FOCUS
LESSON OVERVIEW
Objective: To identify complex sentences and subordinate clauses

_____ Bellringer and Motivating Activity, TWE p. 468

TEACH
_____ Teaching Tip, TWE p. 468
_____ Enabling Strategies: LEP, TWE p. 469

PRACTICE AND ASSESS
_____ Answers to Exercise 3, TWE p. 469

Independent Practice
_____ *Grammar Practice*, p. 32 *
_____ *Grammar Enrichment*, p. 32 *
_____ **Grammar Workbook,** Lesson 43

CLOSE
_____ Close activity, TWE p. 469

* Teacher's Classroom Resources

Unit Assessment

_____ *Tests with Answer Key*
Unit 14 Pretest, pp. 53–54
_____ *Test Generator*
Unit 14 Pretest
You may wish to administer the
Unit 14 Pretest at this point.

• *Homework Assignments* •

_____
_____
_____
_____
_____
_____
_____
_____

Unit 14 Clauses and Complex Sentences *SE/TWE pp. 465–484*

Teacher's Name _____ Date _____

Grade _____ Class(es) _____ Date(s)_____ M Tu W Th F

LESSON 14.3 *pp. 470–471*

FOCUS
LESSON OVERVIEW
Objective: To identify adjective clauses and the relative pronouns that usually introduce adjective clauses

_____ Bellringer and Motivating Activity, TWE p. 470

TEACH
_____ Teaching Tip, TWE p. 470
_____ Enabling Strategies: LEP, TWE p. 471

PRACTICE AND ASSESS
_____ Answers to Exercises 4 and 5, TWE p. 471

Independent Practice
_____ *Grammar Practice,* p. 33 *
_____ *Grammar Reteaching,* p. 33 *
_____ *Grammar Enrichment,* p. 33 *
_____ **Grammar Workbook,** Lesson 44

CLOSE
_____ Close activity, TWE p. 471

LESSON 14.4 *pp. 472–473*

FOCUS
LESSON OVERVIEW
Objective: To use adverb clauses appropriately

_____ Bellringer and Motivating Activity, TWE p. 472

TEACH
_____ Grammar Tip, TWE p. 472
_____ Cross-reference: Grammar, TWE p. 472
_____ Enabling Strategies: LEP, TWE p. 473

PRACTICE AND ASSESS
_____ Answers to Exercises 6 and 7, TWE p. 473

Independent Practice
_____ *Grammar Practice,* p. 34 *
_____ *Grammar Reteaching,* p. 34 *
_____ *Grammar Enrichment,* p. 34 *
_____ **Grammar Workbook,** Lesson 45

• *Homework Assignments* •

_____
_____
_____
_____
_____
_____
_____
_____

CLOSE
_____ Close activity, TWE p. 473

* Teacher's Classroom Resources

Unit 14 Clauses and Complex Sentences *SE/TWE pp. 465–484*

Teacher's Name _____ Date _____

Grade _____ Class(es) _____ Date(s)_____ M Tu W Th F

LESSON 14.5 *pp. 474–475*

FOCUS
LESSON OVERVIEW
Objective: To identify noun clauses and use them appropriately

_____ Bellringer and Motivating Activity, TWE p. 474

TEACH
_____ Teaching Tip, TWE p. 474
_____ Enabling Strategies: LEP, TWE p. 475

PRACTICE AND ASSESS
_____ Answers to Exercises 8 and 9, TWE p. 475

Independent Practice
_____ *Grammar Practice,* p. 35 *
_____ *Grammar Reteaching,* p. 35 *
_____ *Grammar Enrichment,* p. 35 *
_____ **Grammar Workbook,** Lesson 46

CLOSE
_____ Close activity, TWE p. 475

* Teacher's Classroom Resources

UNIT 14 REVIEW *pp. 476–483*

TEACH
_____ About the Literature, TWE p. 476
_____ Linking Grammar and Literature, TWE p. 476
_____ Teaching Tip, TWE p. 476
_____ About the Art, TWE p. 482

PRACTICE AND ASSESS
_____ Answers to Exercises 1–11, TWE p. 477–483

CLOSE
_____ Close activity, TWE p. 483

Writing Application *p. 484*
_____ Sentence Variety in Writing, TWE p. 484
_____ Techniques in Sentence Variety, TWE p. 484
_____ Practice, TWE p. 484

• Homework Assignments •

_____
_____
_____
_____
_____
_____
_____
_____

Unit Assessment

_____ *Tests with Answer Key*
　　　Unit 14 Mastery Test, pp. 55–56
_____ *Test Generator*
　　　Unit 14 Mastery Test
You may wish to administer the
Unit 14 Mastery Test at this point.

Unit 15 Verbals *SE/TWE 485–498*

Teacher's Name _____ Date _____

Grade _____ Class(es) _____ Date(s)_____ M Tu W Th F

LESSON 15.1 *pp. 486–487*

FOCUS
LESSON OVERVIEW
Objective: To identify present and past participles and participial phrases and to punctuate participial phrases correctly

_____ Bellringer and Motivating Activity, TWE p. 486

TEACH
_____ Grammar Tip, TWE p. 486
_____ Cross-reference: Grammar, TWE p. 486
_____ Enabling Strategies: LEP, TWE p. 487
_____ Enabling Strategies: L2, TWE p. 487

PRACTICE AND ASSESS
_____ Answers to Exercises 1 and 2, TWE p. 487

Independent Practice
_____ *Grammar Practice,* p. 36 *
_____ *Grammar Reteaching,* p. 36 *
_____ *Grammar Enrichment,* p. 36 *
_____ **Grammar Workbook,** Lesson 47

CLOSE
_____ Close activity, TWE p. 487

LESSON 15.2 *pp. 488–489*

FOCUS
LESSON OVERVIEW
Objective: To identify and use gerunds and gerund phrases

_____ Bellringer and Motivating Activity, TWE p. 488

TEACH
_____ Teaching Tip, TWE p. 488
_____ Enabling Strategies: LEP, TWE p. 489

PRACTICE AND ASSESS
_____ Answers to Exercises 3 and 4, TWE p. 489

Independent Practice
_____ *Grammar Practice,* p. 37 *
_____ *Grammar Reteaching,* p. 37 *
_____ *Grammar Enrichment,* p. 37 *
_____ **Grammar Workbook,** Lesson 48

Unit Assessment

_____ *Tests with Answer Key*
Unit 15 Pretest, pp. 57–58
_____ *Test Generator*
Unit 15 Pretest
You may wish to administer the Unit 15 Pretest at this point.

• Homework Assignments •

_____

_____

_____

_____

_____

_____

_____

_____

CLOSE
_____ Close activity, TWE p. 489

* Teacher's Classroom Resources

Unit 15 Verbals SE/TWE 485–498

Teacher's Name _____ Date _____

Grade _____ Class(es) _____ Date(s)_____ M Tu W Th F

LESSON 15.3 *pp. 490–491*

FOCUS
LESSON OVERVIEW

Objective: To identify infinitives and infinitive phrases used as nouns and to distinguish infinitives from prepositional phrases that begin with *to*

_____ Bellringer and Motivating Activity, TWE p. 490

TEACH
_____ Teaching Tip, TWE p. 490

_____ Cross-reference: Grammar, TWE p. 490

_____ Enabling Strategies: LEP, TWE p. 491

PRACTICE AND ASSESS
_____ Answers to Exercises 5 and 6, TWE p. 491

Independent Practice

_____ *Grammar Practice,* p. 38 *

_____ *Grammar Reteaching,* p. 38 *

_____ *Grammar Enrichment,* p. 38 *

_____ **Grammar Workbook,** Lesson 49

CLOSE
_____ Close activity, TWE p. 491

* Teacher's Classroom Resources

> ### • Homework Assignments •
>
> _____
> _____
> _____
> _____
> _____
> _____
> _____
> _____

UNIT 15 REVIEW *pp. 492–497*

TEACH
_____ About the Literature, TWE p. 492

_____ Linking Grammar and Literature, TWE p. 492

_____ About the Art, TWE p. 497

PRACTICE AND ASSESS
_____ Answers to Exercises 1–8, TWE p. 493–496

CLOSE
_____ Close activity, TWE p. 497

Writing Application *p. 498*

_____ Phrases in Writing, TWE p. 498

_____ Techniques with Phrases, TWE p. 498

_____ Practice, TWE p. 498

> ### Unit Assessment
>
> _____ *Tests with Answer Key*
> Unit 15 Mastery Test, pp. 59–60
>
> _____ *Test Generator*
> Unit 15 Mastery Test
>
> You may wish to administer the
> Unit 15 Mastery Test at this point.

Unit 16 Subject-Verb Agreement *SE/TWE 499–516*

Teacher's Name _____ Date _____

Grade _____ Class(es) _____ Date(s) _____ M Tu W Th F

LESSON 16.1 *pp. 500–501*

FOCUS
LESSON OVERVIEW
Objective: To recognize that verbs must agree with their subjects

_____ Bellringer and Motivating Activity, TWE p. 500

TEACH
_____ Grammar Tip, TWE p. 500
_____ Cross-reference: Grammar, TWE p. 500
_____ Enabling Strategies: LEP, TWE p. 501
_____ Enabling Strategies: L1, TWE p. 501

PRACTICE AND ASSESS
_____ Answers to Exercises 1 and 2, TWE p. 501

Independent Practice
_____ *Grammar Practice,* p. 39 *
_____ *Grammar Reteaching,* p. 38 *
_____ *Grammar Enrichment,* p. 39 *
_____ **Grammar Workbook,** Lesson 50

CLOSE
_____ Close activity, TWE p. 501

LESSON 16.2 *pp. 502–503*

FOCUS
LESSON OVERVIEW
Objective: To use the verb form that agrees with the subject when the subject does not immediately precede the verb

_____ Bellringer, TWE p. 502

TEACH
_____ Enabling Strategies: LEP, TWE p. 503

PRACTICE AND ASSESS
_____ Answers to Exercises 3 and 4, TWE p. 503

Independent Practice
_____ *Grammar Practice,* p. 40 *
_____ *Grammar Reteaching,* p. 39 *
_____ *Grammar Enrichment,* p. 40 *
_____ **Grammar Workbook,** Lesson 51

CLOSE
_____ Close activity, TWE p. 503

* Teacher's Classroom Resources

Unit Assessment

_____ *Tests with Answer Key*
Unit 16 Pretest, pp. 61–62
_____ *Test Generator*
Unit 16 Pretest
You may wish to administer the Unit 16 Pretest at this point.

• Homework Assignments •

_____
_____
_____
_____
_____
_____
_____
_____

Unit 16 Subject-Verb Agreement SE/TWE 499–516

Teacher's Name _____ Date _____

Grade _____ Class(es) _____ Date(s)_____ M Tu W Th F

LESSON 16.3 *pp. 504–505*

FOCUS
LESSON OVERVIEW
Objective: To use verbs that agree in number with special subjects such as collective nouns, numbers, titles, and nouns with unusual endings

_____ Bellringer and Motivating Activity, TWE p. 504

TEACH
_____ Grammar Tip, TWE p. 504
_____ Cross-reference: Grammar, TWE p. 504
_____ Enabling Strategies: LEP, TWE p. 505

PRACTICE AND ASSESS
_____ Answers to Exercises 5 and 6, TWE p. 505

Independent Practice
_____ *Grammar Practice,* p. 41 *
_____ *Grammar Reteaching,* p. 40 *
_____ *Grammar Enrichment,* p. 41 *
_____ **Grammar Workbook,** Lesson 52

CLOSE
_____ Close activity, TWE p. 505

LESSON 16.4 *pp. 506–507*

FOCUS
LESSON OVERVIEW
Objective: To identify singular and plural indefinite pronouns and use verbs that agree with them in number

_____ Bellringer and Motivating Activity, TWE p. 506

TEACH
_____ Teaching Tip, TWE p. 506
_____ Enabling Strategies: LEP, TWE p. 507

PRACTICE AND ASSESS
_____ Answers to Exercises 7 and 8, TWE p. 507

Independent Practice
_____ *Grammar Practice,* p. 41 *
_____ *Grammar Reteaching,* p. 41 *
_____ *Grammar Enrichment,* p. 41 *
_____ **Grammar Workbook,** Lesson 53

• Homework Assignments •

_____

_____

_____

_____

_____

_____

_____

_____

_____

CLOSE
_____ Close activity, TWE p. 507

* Teacher's Classroom Resources

Unit 16 Subject-Verb Agreement *SE/TWE 499–516*

Teacher's Name _____ Date _____

Grade _____ Class(es) _____ Date(s)_____ M Tu W Th F

LESSON 16.5 *pp. 508–509*

FOCUS
LESSON OVERVIEW
Objective: To use the appropriate verb form with compound subjects

_____ Bellringer and Motivating Activity, TWE p. 508

TEACH
_____ Cross-reference: Grammar, TWE p. 508
_____ Enabling Strategies: LEP, TWE p. 509

PRACTICE AND ASSESS
_____ Answers to Exercise 9, TWE p. 509

Independent Practice
_____ *Grammar Practice*, p. 39 *
_____ *Grammar Enrichment*, p. 39 *
_____ **Grammar Workbook**, Lesson 54

CLOSE
_____ Close activity, TWE p. 509

* Teacher's Classroom Resources

> ### • Homework Assignments •
>
> _____
> _____
> _____
> _____
> _____
> _____
> _____
> _____

UNIT 16 REVIEW *pp. 510–515*

TEACH
_____ About the Literature, TWE p. 510
_____ Linking Grammar and Literature, TWE p. 510
_____ Teaching Tip, TWE p. 510
_____ About the Art, TWE p. 514

PRACTICE AND ASSESS
_____ Answers to Exercises 1–8, TWE p. 511–515

CLOSE
_____ Close activity, TWE p. 515

Writing Application *p. 516*
_____ Subject-Verb Agreement in Writing, TWE p. 516
_____ Techniques with Subject-Verb Agreement, TWE p. 516
_____ Practice, TWE p. 516

> ### Unit Assessment
>
> _____ *Tests with Answer Key*
> Unit 16 Mastery Test, pp. 63–64
> _____ *Test Generator*
> Unit 16 Mastery Test
> You may wish to administer the
> Unit 16 Mastery Test at this point.

Unit 17 Glossary of Special Usage Problems

SE/TWE pp. 517–526

Teacher's Name _____ Date _____

Grade _____ Class(es) _____ Date(s)_____ M Tu W Th F

LESSON 17.1 *pp. 518–519*

FOCUS
LESSON OVERVIEW
Objective: To understand the differences in meaning and usage between some commonly confused words

_____ Bellringer and Motivating Activity, TWE p. 518

TEACH
_____ Vocabulary Link, TWE p. 518
_____ Enabling Strategies: LEP, TWE p. 519

PRACTICE AND ASSESS
_____ Answers to Exercises 1 and 2, TWE p. 519

Independent Practice
_____ *Grammar Practice,* p. 42 *
_____ *Grammar Reteaching,* p. 42 *
_____ *Grammar Enrichment,* p. 42 *
_____ **Grammar Workbook,** Lessons 63–65

CLOSE
_____ Close activity, TWE p. 519

LESSON 17.2 *pp. 520–521*

FOCUS
LESSON OVERVIEW
Objective: To use the troublesome words introduced in the lesson correctly

_____ Bellringer and Motivating Activity, TWE p. 520

TEACH
_____ Technology Tip, TWE p. 520
_____ Cross-reference: Composition, TWE p. 520
_____ Enabling Strategies: LEP, TWE p. 521

PRACTICE AND ASSESS
_____ Answers to Exercises 3 and 4, TWE p. 521

Independent Practice
_____ *Grammar Practice,* p. 42 *
_____ *Grammar Reteaching,* p. 42 *
_____ *Grammar Enrichment,* p. 42 *
_____ **Grammar Workbook,** Lessons 65–67

Unit Assessment

_____ *Tests with Answer Key*
Unit 17 Pretest, pp. 65–66
_____ *Test Generator*
Unit 17 Pretest
You may wish to administer the Unit 17 Pretest at this point.

• Homework Assignments •

_____
_____
_____
_____
_____
_____
_____
_____
_____

CLOSE
_____ Close activity, TWE p. 521

* Teacher's Classroom Resources

Unit 17 Glossary of Special Usage Problems

SE/TWE pp. 517–526

Teacher's Name _____ Date _____

Grade _____ Class(es) _____ Date(s)_____ M Tu W Th F

UNIT 17 REVIEW *pp. 522–525*

TEACH
_____ About the Literature, TWE p. 522
_____ Linking Grammar and Literature, TWE p. 522
_____ Teaching Tip, TWE p. 522
_____ About the Art, TWE p. 525

PRACTICE AND ASSESS
_____ Answers to Exercises 1–3, TWE p. 523–525

CLOSE
_____ Close activity, TWE p. 525

Writing Application *p. 526*
_____ Usage in Writing, TWE p. 526
_____ Techniques with Usage, TWE p. 526
_____ Practice, TWE p. 526

> ### Unit Assessment
>
> _____ *Tests with Answer Key*
> Unit 17 Mastery Test, pp. 67–68
> _____ *Test Generator*
> Unit 17 Mastery Test
> You may wish to administer the
> Unit 17 Mastery Test at this point.

Unit 18 Diagraming Sentences *SE/TWE pp. 527–536*

Teacher's Name _____ Date _____

Grade _____ Class(es) _____ Date(s) _____ M Tu W Th F

LESSON 18.1 *p. 528*

TEACH
_____ Teaching Tip, TWE p. 528

PRACTICE AND ASSESS
_____ Answers to Exercise 1, TWE p. 528

CLOSE
_____ Close activity, TWE p. 528

LESSON 18.2 *p. 529*

PRACTICE AND ASSESS
_____ Answers to Exercise 2, TWE p. 529

CLOSE
_____ Close activity, TWE p. 529

LESSON 18.3 *p. 530*

TEACH
_____ Cross-reference: Grammar, TWE p. 530

PRACTICE AND ASSESS
_____ Answers to Exercise 3, TWE p. 530

CLOSE
_____ Close activity, TWE p. 530

LESSON 18.4 *p. 531*

PRACTICE AND ASSESS
_____ Answers to Exercise 4, TWE p. 531

CLOSE
_____ Close activity, TWE p. 531

Unit Assessment

_____ *Tests with Answer Key*
Unit 18 Pretest, pp. 69–70
_____ *Test Generator*
Unit 18 Pretest
You may wish to administer the
Unit 18 Pretest at this point.

• Homework Assignments •

_____
_____
_____
_____
_____
_____
_____
_____

Unit 18 Diagraming Sentences *SE/TWE pp. 527–536*

Teacher's Name _____ Date _____
Grade _____ Class(es) _____ Date(s)_____ M Tu W Th F

LESSON 18.5 *p. 532*

PRACTICE AND ASSESS
_____ Answers to Exercise 5, TWE p. 532

CLOSE
_____ Close activity, TWE p. 532

LESSON 18.6 *p. 533*

TEACH
_____ Grammar Tip, TWE p. 533

PRACTICE AND ASSESS
_____ Answers to Exercise 6, TWE p. 533

CLOSE
_____ Close activity, TWE p. 533

LESSON 18.7 *p. 534*

TEACH
_____ Teaching Tip, TWE p. 534

PRACTICE AND ASSESS
_____ Answers to Exercise 7, TWE p. 534

CLOSE
_____ Close activity, TWE p. 534

LESSON 18.8 *p. 535*

PRACTICE AND ASSESS
_____ Answers to Exercise 8, TWE p. 535

LESSON 18.9 *p. 536*

PRACTICE AND ASSESS
_____ Answers to Exercise 9, TWE p. 536

CLOSE
_____ Close activity, TWE p. 536

• Homework Assignments •

_____
_____
_____
_____
_____
_____
_____
_____

Unit Assessment

_____ *Tests with Answer Key*
Unit 18 Mastery Test, pp. 71–72
_____ *Test Generator*
Unit 18 Mastery Test
You may wish to administer the
Unit 18 Mastery Test at this point.

Unit 19 Capitalization *SE/TWE pp. 537–552*

Teacher's Name _____ Date _____

Grade _____ Class(es) _____ Date(s)_____ M Tu W Th F

LESSON 19.1 *pp. 538–539*

FOCUS
LESSON OVERVIEW
Objective: To capitalize sentences, quotations, and salutations correctly

_____ Bellringer and Motivating Activity, TWE p. 538

TEACH
_____ Teaching Tip, TWE p. 538
_____ Enabling Strategies: LEP, TWE p. 539

PRACTICE AND ASSESS
_____ Answers to Exercise 1, TWE p. 539

Independent Practice
_____ *Grammar Practice*, p. 43 *
_____ *Grammar Reteaching*, p. 43 *
_____ *Grammar Enrichment*, p. 43 *
_____ **Grammar Workbook,** Lesson 68

CLOSE
_____ Close activity, TWE p. 539

LESSON 19.2 *pp. 540–541*

FOCUS
LESSON OVERVIEW
Objective: To recognize correct capitalization of names and titles of people

_____ Bellringer and Motivating Activity, TWE p. 540

TEACH
_____ Grammar Tip, TWE p. 540
_____ Enabling Strategies: LEP, TWE p. 541

PRACTICE AND ASSESS
_____ Answers to Exercises 2 and 3, TWE p. 541

Independent Practice
_____ *Grammar Practice*, p. 43 *
_____ *Grammar Reteaching*, p. 44 *
_____ *Grammar Enrichment*, p. 43 *
_____ **Grammar Workbook,** Lesson 69

CLOSE
_____ Close activity, TWE p. 541

* Teacher's Classroom Resources

Unit Assessment

_____ *Tests with Answer Key*
Unit 19 Pretest, pp. 73–74
_____ *Test Generator*
Unit 19 Pretest
You may wish to administer the Unit 19 Pretest at this point.

• Homework Assignments •

_____
_____
_____
_____
_____
_____
_____
_____

Unit 19 Capitalization *SE/TWE pp. 537–552*

Teacher's Name _____ Date _____

Grade _____ Class(es) _____ Date(s) _____ M Tu W Th F

LESSON 19.3 *pp. 542–543*

FOCUS
LESSON OVERVIEW
Objective: To recognize and capitalize the names of specific places

_____ Bellringer and Motivating Activity, TWE p. 542

TEACH
_____ Teaching Tip, TWE p. 542
_____ Enabling Strategies: LEP, TWE p. 543

PRACTICE AND ASSESS
_____ Answers to Exercises 4 and 5, TWE p. 543

Independent Practice
_____ *Grammar Practice*, p. 44 *
_____ *Grammar Reteaching*, p. 44 *
_____ *Grammar Enrichment*, p. 44 *
_____ **Grammar Workbook**, Lesson 70

CLOSE
_____ Close activity, TWE p. 543

LESSON 19.4 *pp. 544–545*

FOCUS
LESSON OVERVIEW
Objective: To identify correct capitalization of proper nouns and adjectives

_____ Bellringer and Motivating Activity, TWE p. 544

TEACH
_____ Teaching Tip, TWE p. 544
_____ Cross-reference: Mechanics, TWE p. 544
_____ Enabling Strategies: LEP, TWE p. 545

PRACTICE AND ASSESS
_____ Answers to Exercises 6 and 7, TWE p. 545

Independent Practice
_____ *Grammar Practice*, p. 44 *
_____ *Grammar Reteaching*, p. 44 *
_____ *Grammar Enrichment*, p. 44 *
_____ **Grammar Workbook**, Lesson 71

• Homework Assignments •

_____
_____
_____
_____
_____
_____
_____
_____
_____

CLOSE
_____ Close activity, TWE p. 545

* Teacher's Classroom Resources

Unit 19 Capitalization *SE/TWE pp. 537–552*

Teacher's Name _____ Date _____

Grade _____ Class(es) _____ Date(s) _____ M Tu W Th F

UNIT 19 REVIEW *pp. 546–551*

TEACH
_____ About the Literature, TWE p. 546
_____ Linking Grammar and Literature, TWE p. 546
_____ Teaching Tip, TWE p. 546
_____ About the Art, TWE p. 550

PRACTICE AND ASSESS
_____ Answers to Exercises 1–8, TWE p. 547–551

CLOSE
_____ Close activity, TWE p. 551

Writing Application *p. 552*
_____ Capitalization in Writing, TWE p. 552
_____ Techniques with Capitalization, TWE p. 552
_____ Practice, TWE p. 552

Unit Assessment
_____ *Tests with Answer Key*
Unit 19 Mastery Test, pp. 75–76
_____ *Test Generator*
Unit 19 Mastery Test
You may wish to administer the
Unit 19 Mastery Test at this point.

Unit 20 Punctuation *SE/TWE pp. 553–582*

Teacher's Name _____ Date _____

Grade _____ Class(es) _____ Date(s)_____ M Tu W Th F

LESSON 20.1 *pp. 554–555*

FOCUS
LESSON OVERVIEW
Objective: To use periods at the end of declarative and imperative sentences, question marks at the end of interrogative sentences, and exclamation points at the end of exclamatory sentences and after interjections

_____ Bellringer and Motivating Activity, TWE p. 554

TEACH
_____ Enabling Strategies: LEP, TWE p. 555

PRACTICE AND ASSESS
_____ Answers to Exercise 1, TWE p. 555

Independent Practice
_____ *Grammar Practice,* p. 45 *
_____ *Grammar Reteaching,* p. 45 *
_____ *Grammar Enrichment,* p. 45 *
_____ **Grammar Workbook,** Lesson 72

CLOSE
_____ Close activity, TWE p. 555

LESSON 20.2 *pp. 556–557*

FOCUS
LESSON OVERVIEW
Objective: To use commas in a series and to set off introductory and interrupting words and phrases

_____ Bellringer and Motivating Activity, TWE p. 556

TEACH
_____ Teaching Tip, TWE p. 556
_____ Enabling Strategies: LEP, TWE p. 557

PRACTICE AND ASSESS
_____ Answers to Exercise 2, TWE p. 557

Independent Practice
_____ *Grammar Practice,* p. 46 *
_____ *Grammar Reteaching,* p. 46 *
_____ *Grammar Enrichment,* p. 46 *
_____ **Grammar Workbook,** Lesson 73

CLOSE
_____ Close activity, TWE p. 557

* Teacher's Classroom Resources

> **• Homework Assignments •**
>
> _____
> _____
> _____
> _____
> _____
> _____
> _____
> _____

Unit 20 Punctuation *SE/TWE pp. 553–582*

Teacher's Name _____ Date _____

Grade _____ Class(es) _____ Date(s)_____ M Tu W Th F

LESSON 20.3 *pp. 558–559*

FOCUS
LESSON OVERVIEW
Objective: To recognize the appropriate use of commas in compound sentences and after introductory adverb clauses

_____ Bellringer and Motivating Activity, TWE p. 558

TEACH
_____ Enabling Strategies: LEP, TWE p. 559

PRACTICE AND ASSESS
_____ Answers to Exercise 3, TWE p. 559

Independent Practice
_____ *Grammar Practice*, p. 47 *
_____ *Grammar Reteaching*, p. 47 *
_____ *Grammar Enrichment*, p. 47 *
_____ **Grammar Workbook,** Lesson 74

CLOSE
_____ Close activity, TWE p. 559

┌─────────────────────────────┐
│ **• Homework Assignments •** │
│   │
│ _____ │
│ _____ │
│ _____ │
│ _____ │
│ _____ │
│ _____ │
│ _____ │
│ _____ │
└─────────────────────────────┘

LESSON 20.4 *pp. 560–561*

FOCUS
LESSON OVERVIEW
Objective: To use commas appropriately

_____ Bellringer and Motivating Activity, TWE p. 560

TEACH
_____ Enabling Strategies: LEP, TWE p. 561

PRACTICE AND ASSESS
_____ Answers to Exercises 4 and 5, TWE p. 561

Independent Practice
_____ *Grammar Practice*, p. 48 *
_____ *Grammar Reteaching*, p. 48 *
_____ *Grammar Enrichment*, p. 48 *
_____ **Grammar Workbook,** Lessons 75–76

CLOSE
_____ Close activity, TWE p. 561

* Teacher's Classroom Resources

Unit 20 Punctuation *SE/TWE pp. 553–582*

Teacher's Name _____ Date _____

Grade _____ Class(es) _____ Date(s)_____ M Tu W Th F

LESSON 20.5 *pp. 562–563*

FOCUS
LESSON OVERVIEW
Objective: To use semicolons to separate main clauses and series that contain commas; to use colons to introduce lists, to separate hour and minute, and to end salutations in business letters

_____ Bellringer and Motivating Activity, TWE p. 562

TEACH
_____ Enabling Strategies: LEP, TWE p. 563

PRACTICE AND ASSESS
_____ Answers to Exercises 6 and 7, TWE p. 563

Independent Practice
_____ *Grammar Practice,* p. 49 *
_____ *Grammar Reteaching,* p. 49 *
_____ *Grammar Enrichment,* p. 49 *
_____ **Grammar Workbook,** Lesson 78

CLOSE
_____ Close activity, TWE p. 563

LESSON 20.6 *pp. 564–565*

FOCUS
LESSON OVERVIEW
Objective: To use quotation marks and punctuation appropriately with direct quotations and titles of short works and to use italics (or underlining) appropriately

_____ Bellringer and Motivating Activity, TWE p. 564

TEACH
_____ Cross-reference: Mechanics, TWE p. 564
_____ Enabling Strategies: LEP, TWE p. 565

PRACTICE AND ASSESS
_____ Answers to Exercises 8 and 9, TWE p. 565

Independent Practice
_____ *Grammar Practice,* p. 50 *
_____ *Grammar Reteaching,* p. 50 *
_____ *Grammar Enrichment,* p. 50 *
_____ **Grammar Workbook,** Lessons 79–81

• Homework Assignments •

_____
_____
_____
_____
_____
_____
_____
_____

CLOSE
_____ Close activity, TWE p. 565

* Teacher's Classroom Resources

Unit 20 Punctuation *SE/TWE pp. 553–582*

Teacher's Name _____ Date _____

Grade _____ Class(es) _____ Date(s)_____ M Tu W Th F

LESSON 20.7 *pp. 566–567*

FOCUS
LESSON OVERVIEW
Objective: To use apostrophes with contractions, special plurals, and possessives

_____ Bellringer and Motivating Activity, TWE p. 566

TEACH
_____ Cross-reference: Grammar, TWE p. 566
_____ Enabling Strategies: LEP, TWE p. 567

PRACTICE AND ASSESS
_____ Answers to Exercises 10 and 11, TWE p. 567

Independent Practice
_____ *Grammar Practice,* p. 51 *
_____ *Grammar Reteaching,* p. 51 *
_____ *Grammar Enrichment,* p. 51 *
_____ **Grammar Workbook,** Lesson 82

LESSON 20.8 *pp. 568–569*

FOCUS
LESSON OVERVIEW
Objective: To recognize the correct use of hyphens, dashes, and parentheses

_____ Bellringer and Motivating Activity, TWE p. 568

TEACH
_____ Teaching Tip, TWE p. 568
_____ Enabling Strategies: LEP, TWE p. 569

PRACTICE AND ASSESS
_____ Answers to Exercises 12 and 13, TWE p. 569

Independent Practice
_____ *Grammar Practice,* p. 51 *
_____ *Grammar Reteaching,* p. 51 *
_____ *Grammar Enrichment,* p. 51 *
_____ **Grammar Workbook,** Lesson 83

CLOSE
_____ Close activity, TWE p. 569

* Teacher's Classroom Resources

> **• Homework Assignments •**
>
> _____
> _____
> _____
> _____
> _____
> _____
> _____
> _____

Unit 20 Punctuation *SE/TWE pp. 553–582*

Teacher's Name _____ Date _____

Grade _____ Class(es) _____ Date(s)_____ M Tu W Th F

LESSON 20.9 *pp. 570–571*

FOCUS
LESSON OVERVIEW
Objective: To recognize the correct use and form of abbreviations

_____ Bellringer and Motivating Activity, TWE p. 570

TEACH
_____ Vocabulary Link, TWE p. 570
_____ Enabling Strategies: LEP, TWE p. 571

PRACTICE AND ASSESS
_____ Answers to Exercises 14 and 15, TWE p. 571

Independent Practice
_____ *Grammar Practice,* p. 52 *
_____ *Grammar Reteaching,* p. 52 *
_____ *Grammar Enrichment,* p. 52 *
_____ **Grammar Workbook,** Lesson 84

CLOSE
_____ Close activity, TWE p. 571

LESSON 20.10 *pp. 572–573*

FOCUS
LESSON OVERVIEW
Objective: To recognize the correct use of numbers and numerals

_____ Bellringer and Motivating Activity, TWE p. 572

TEACH
_____ Vocabulary Link, TWE p. 572
_____ Enabling Strategies: LEP, TWE p. 573
_____ Enabling Strategies: L3, TWE p. 573

PRACTICE AND ASSESS
_____ Answers to Exercise 16, TWE p. 573

Independent Practice
_____ *Grammar Practice,* p. 52 *
_____ *Grammar Reteaching,* p. 52 *
_____ *Grammar Enrichment,* p. 52 *
_____ **Grammar Workbook,** Lesson 85

CLOSE
_____ Close activity, TWE p. 573

* Teacher's Classroom Resources

• Homework Assignments •
_____
_____
_____
_____
_____
_____
_____
_____

Unit 20 Punctuation *SE/TWE pp. 553–582*

Teacher's Name _____ Date _____

Grade _____ Class(es) _____ Date(s)_____ M Tu W Th F

UNIT 20 REVIEW *pp. 574–581*

TEACH
_____ About the Literature, TWE p. 574
_____ Linking Grammar and Literature, TWE p. 574
_____ Teaching Tip, TWE p. 574
_____ Teaching Tip, TWE p. 574
_____ About the Art, TWE p. 581

PRACTICE AND ASSESS
_____ Answers to Exercises 1–12, TWE p. 575–580

CLOSE
_____ Close activity, TWE p. 581

Writing Application *p. 582*
_____ Quotation Marks in Writing, TWE p. 582
_____ Techniques with Quotation Marks, TWE p. 582
_____ Practice, TWE p. 582

Unit Assessment
_____ *Tests with Answer Key*
Unit 20 Mastery Test, pp. 79–80
_____ *Test Generator*
Unit 20 Mastery Test
You may wish to administer the
Unit 20 Mastery Test at this point.

Unit 21 Grammar Through Sentence Combining

SE/TWE pp. 583–592

Teacher's Name _____ Date _____

Grade _____ Class(es) _____ Date(s) _____ M Tu W Th F

LESSON 21.1 *pp. 584–585*

FOCUS
LESSON OVERVIEW
Objective: To recognize and use prepositional phrases correctly

_____ Bellringer and Motivating Activity, TWE p. 584

TEACH
_____ Cross-reference: Grammar, TWE p. 584
_____ Enabling Strategies: LEP, TWE p. 585

PRACTICE AND ASSESS
_____ Answers to Exercises 1 and 2, TWE p. 585

Independent Practice
_____ *Sentence Combining Practice*, p. 5 *
_____ **Grammar Workbook**, Lesson 38

CLOSE
_____ Close activity, TWE p. 585

LESSON 21.2 *pp. 586–587*

FOCUS
LESSON OVERVIEW
Objective: To recognize and use appositives and appositive phrases

_____ Bellringer and Motivating Activity, TWE p. 586

TEACH
_____ Teaching Tip, TWE p. 586
_____ Enabling Strategies: LEP, TWE p. 587

PRACTICE AND ASSESS
_____ Answers to Exercises 3 and 4, TWE p. 587

Independent Practice
_____ *Sentence Combining Practice*, pp. 7–8 *
_____ *Grammar Practice*, p. 52 *
_____ *Grammar Reteaching*, p. 52 *
_____ *Grammar Enrichment*, p. 52 *
_____ **Grammar Workbook**, Lesson 11

CLOSE
_____ Close activity, TWE p. 587

* Teacher's Classroom Resources

Unit Assessment

_____ *Tests with Answer Key*
Unit 21 Pretest, pp. 81–82
_____ *Test Generator*
Unit 21 Pretest
You may wish to administer the Unit 21 Pretest at this point.

• Homework Assignments •

_____
_____
_____
_____
_____
_____
_____
_____
_____

Unit 21 Grammar Through Sentence Combining

SE/TWE pp. 583–592

Teacher's Name _____ Date _____

Grade _____ Class(es) _____ Date(s)_____ M Tu W Th F

LESSON 21.3 *pp. 588–589*

FOCUS
LESSON OVERVIEW
Objective: To use adjective clauses correctly in combining sentences

_____ Bellringer, TWE p. 588

TEACH
_____ Enabling Strategies: LEP, TWE p. 589

PRACTICE AND ASSESS
_____ Answers to Exercises 5 and 6, TWE p. 589

Independent Practice
_____ *Sentence Combining Practice,* pp. 14–15 *
_____ **Grammar Workbook,** Lesson 44

CLOSE
_____ Close activity, TWE p. 589

LESSON 21.4 *pp. 590–592*

FOCUS
LESSON OVERVIEW
Objective: To recognize adverb clauses and use them correctly in combining sentences

_____ Bellringer and Motivating Activity, TWE p. 590

TEACH
_____ Vocabulary Link, TWE p. 590
_____ Enabling Strategies: LEP, TWE p. 591
_____ Enabling Strategies: L1, TWE p. 592

PRACTICE AND ASSESS
_____ Answers to Exercises 7 through 9, TWE pp. 591–592

Independent Practice
_____ *Sentence Combining Practice,* pp. 18–20 *
_____ **Grammar Workbook,** Lesson 45

CLOSE
_____ Close activity, TWE p. 592

* Teacher's Classroom Resources

• Homework Assignments •

_____
_____
_____
_____
_____
_____
_____
_____
_____

Unit Assessment

_____ *Tests with Answer Key*
Unit 21 Mastery Test, pp. 83–84
_____ *Test Generator*
Unit 21 Mastery Test
You may wish to administer the
Unit 21 Mastery Test at this point.

Unit 22 Library and Reference Resources

SE/TWE pp. 595–616

Teacher's Name _____ Date _____

Grade _____ Class(es) _____ Date(s)_____ M Tu W Th F

LESSON 22.1 *pp. 595–597*

FOCUS
LESSON OVERVIEW
Objective: To become familiar with the arrangement of a library

_____ Bellringer and Motivating Activity, TWE p. 595

TEACH
Guided Practice
_____ L2, Finding Materials, TWE p. 596
_____ L1, Making a Chart, TWE p. 596
_____ Connections Across the Curriculum: History, TWE p. 596
_____ Visual Thinking, TWE p. 597

PRACTICE AND ASSESS
_____ Answers to Exercise 1, TWE p. 597

Independent Practice
_____ *Thinking and Study Skills*, pp. 28–29 *
_____ *Vocabulary and Spelling Practice*, pp. 35–40 *

CLOSE
_____ Close activity, TWE p. 597

LESSON 22.2 *pp. 598–599*

FOCUS
LESSON OVERVIEW
Objective: To become familiar with the Dewey Decimal System

_____ Bellringer and Motivating Activity, TWE p. 598

TEACH
Guided Practice
_____ L2, Using the Dewey Decimal System, TWE p. 599
_____ Connections Across the Curriculum: History, TWE p. 599

PRACTICE AND ASSESS
_____ Evaluation Guidelines for Exercise 2, TWE p. 599

Independent Practice
_____ *Thinking and Study Skills*, pp. 28–29 *
_____ *Vocabulary and Spelling Practice*, pp. 35–40 *

Unit Assessment

_____ *Tests with Answer Key*
Unit 22 Pretest, pp. 85–86
_____ *Test Generator*
Unit 22 Pretest
You may wish to administer the Unit 22 Pretest at this point.

• Homework Assignments •

_____

_____

_____

_____

_____

_____

_____

_____

CLOSE
_____ Close activity, TWE p. 599

* Teacher's Classroom Resources

Unit 22 Library and Reference Resources

SE/TWE pp. 595–616

Teacher's Name _____ Date _____

Grade _____ Class(es) _____ Date(s)_____ M Tu W Th F

LESSON 22.3 *pp. 600–602*

FOCUS
LESSON OVERVIEW
Objective: To learn to use card and computer catalogs

_____ Bellringer and Motivating Activity, TWE p. 600

TEACH
Guided Practice
_____ L1, Creating Catalog Cards, TWE p. 601
_____ L3, Investigating a Computer Catalog, TWE p. 601
_____ Beyond the Classroom, TWE p. 601
_____ Cooperative Learning, TWE p. 602

PRACTICE AND ASSESS
_____ Evaluation Guidelines for Exercise 3, TWE p. 602

Independent Practice
_____ *Thinking and Study Skills*, pp. 28–29 *
_____ *Vocabulary and Spelling Practice*, pp. 35–40 *

LESSON 22.4 *pp. 603–606*

FOCUS
LESSON OVERVIEW
Objective: To become familiar with basic reference books

_____ Bellringer and Motivating Activity, TWE p. 603

TEACH
Guided Practice
_____ L1, Making a Chart, TWE p. 604
_____ Cross-reference: Writing, TWE p. 604
_____ Enabling Strategies: LEP, TWE p. 604
_____ L3, Researching Atlases, TWE p. 605
_____ Enrichment and Extension, TWE p. 605
_____ Technology Tip, TWE p. 606

PRACTICE AND ASSESS
_____ Answers to Exercise 4, TWE p. 606

Independent Practice
_____ *Thinking and Study Skills*, pp. 28–29 *
_____ *Vocabulary and Spelling Practice*, pp. 35–40 *

CLOSE
_____ Close activity, TWE p. 602

• *Homework Assignments* •

_____
_____
_____
_____
_____
_____
_____
_____

CLOSE
_____ Close activity, TWE p. 606

* Teacher's Classroom Resources

Unit 22 Library and Reference Resources

SE/TWE pp. 595–616

Teacher's Name _____ Date _____

Grade _____ Class(es) _____ Date(s)_____ M Tu W Th F

LESSON 22.5 *pp. 607–608*

FOCUS
LESSON OVERVIEW
Objective: To become familiar with library resources other than books

_____ Bellringer and Motivating Activity, TWE p. 607

TEACH
Guided Practice
_____ L2, Discussing Print and Nonprint Library Resources, TWE p. 608
_____ Technology Tip, TWE p. 608

PRACTICE AND ASSESS
_____ Answers to Exercise 5, TWE p. 608

Independent Practice
_____ *Thinking and Study Skills*, pp. 28–29 *
_____ *Vocabulary and Spelling Practice*, pp. 35–40 *

CLOSE
_____ Close activity, TWE p. 608

LESSON 22.6 *PP. 609–610*

FOCUS
LESSON OVERVIEW
Objective: To become familiar with using magazines to find information

_____ Bellringer and Motivating Activity, TWE p. 609

TEACH
Guided Practice
_____ L2, Finding Current Information, TWE p. 610
_____ Enabling Strategies: LEP, TWE p. 610

PRACTICE AND ASSESS
_____ Answers to Exercise 6, TWE p. 610

Independent Practice
_____ *Thinking and Study Skills*, pp. 28–29 *
_____ *Vocabulary and Spelling Practice*, pp. 35–40 *

CLOSE
_____ Close activity, TWE p. 610

* Teacher's Classroom Resources

• Homework Assignments •

_____

_____

_____

_____

_____

_____

_____

_____

Unit 22 Library and Reference Resources

SE/TWE pp. 595–616

Teacher's Name _____ Date _____

Grade _____ Class(es) _____ Date(s)_____ M Tu W Th F

LESSON 22.7 *pp. 611–613*

FOCUS
LESSON OVERVIEW

Objective: To become familiar with dictionaries and the thesaurus

_____ Bellringer and Motivating Activity, TWE p. 611

TEACH
Guided Practice

_____ L2, Choosing a Synonym, TWE p. 612
_____ L1, Finding Words in a Dictionary, TWE p. 612
_____ Technology Tip, TWE p. 612
_____ Cultural Diversity, TWE p. 613

PRACTICE AND ASSESS
_____ Answers to Exercise 7, TWE p. 613

Independent Practice

_____ *Thinking and Study Skills*, pp. 28–29 *
_____ *Vocabulary and Spelling Practice*, pp. 35–40 *

LESSON 22.8 *pp. 614–616*

FOCUS
LESSON OVERVIEW

Objective: To become familiar with using a dictionary entry

_____ Bellringer and Motivating Activity, TWE p. 614

TEACH
Guided Practice

_____ L2, Understanding Symbols and Abbreviations, TWE p. 615
_____ L3, Using a Thesaurus, TWE p. 615
_____ Cross-reference: Grammar, Usage, and Mechanics, TWE p. 615
_____ Enabling Strategies: LEP, TWE p. 615
_____ Visual Thinking, TWE p. 616

PRACTICE AND ASSESS
_____ Answers to Exercise 8, TWE p. 616

Independent Practice

_____ *Thinking and Study Skills*, pp. 28–29 *
_____ *Vocabulary and Spelling Practice*, pp. 35–40 *

CLOSE
_____ Close activity, TWE p. 616

* Teacher's Classroom Resources

CLOSE
_____ Close activity, TWE p. 613

```
• Homework Assignments •

_____
_____
_____
_____
_____
_____
_____
_____
_____
```

```
Unit Assessment

_____ Tests with Answer Key
      Unit 22 Mastery Test, pp. 87–88
_____ Test Generator
      Unit 22 Mastery Test
You may wish to administer the
Unit 22 Mastery Test at this point.
```

Unit 23 Vocabulary and Spelling *SE/TWE pp. 617–646*

Teacher's Name _____ Date _____

Grade _____ Class(es) _____ Date(s)_____ M Tu W Th F

LESSON 23.1 *pp. 617–619*

FOCUS
LESSON OVERVIEW
Objective: To become familiar with borrowed words

_____ Bellringer and Motivating Activity, TWE p. 617

TEACH
Guided Practice
_____ L2, Using Borrowed Words, TWE p. 618
_____ L1, Using a Dictionary, TWE p. 618
_____ Connections Across the Curriculum: History, TWE p. 618
_____ Cultural Diversity, TWE p. 619

PRACTICE AND ASSESS
_____ Answers to Exercise 1, TWE p. 619
_____ Evaluation Guidelines for Exercise 2, TWE p. 619
Independent Practice
_____ *Thinking and Study Skills*, pp. 9, 25–27 *
_____ *Vocabulary and Spelling Practice*, pp. 13, 21–26 *

CLOSE
_____ Close activity, TWE p. 619

Unit Assessment
_____ *Tests with Answer Key*
Unit 23 Pretest, pp. 89–90
_____ *Test Generator*
Unit 23 Pretest
You may wish to administer the Unit 23 Pretest at this point.

• Homework Assignments •

_____
_____
_____
_____
_____
_____
_____
_____
_____

WORDWORKS 23.1 *p. 620*
LESSON OVERVIEW
Objective: To become familiar with cognates and word families

TEACH
_____ Discussion, TWE p. 620
_____ L3, Making a Word Family Tree, TWE p. 620
_____ Connections Across the Curriculum: Mathematics/Science, TWE p. 620

PRACTICE AND ASSESS
_____ Answers to Challenge and Pick a Number, TWE p. 620

CLOSE
_____ Close activity, TWE p. 620

* Teacher's Classroom Resources

Unit 23 Vocabulary and Spelling *SE/TWE pp. 617–646*

Teacher's Name _____ Date _____

Grade _____ Class(es) _____ Date(s)_____ M Tu W Th F

LESSON 23.2 *pp. 621–622*

FOCUS
LESSON OVERVIEW
Objective: To become familiar with specific types of context clues

_____ Bellringer and Motivating Activity, TWE p. 621

TEACH
Guided Practice
_____ L2, Understanding Unfamiliar Words, TWE p. 622
_____ Enabling Strategies: LEP, TWE p. 622

PRACTICE AND ASSESS
_____ Answers to Exercise 3, TWE p. 622

Independent Practice
_____ *Thinking and Study Skills*, pp. 9, 25–27 *
_____ *Vocabulary and Spelling Practice*, pp. 13, 21–26 *

CLOSE
_____ Close activity, TWE p. 622

• Homework Assignments •

_____
_____
_____
_____
_____
_____
_____
_____

WORDWORKS 23.2 *p. 623*
LESSON OVERVIEW
Objective: To understand pictographic writing

TEACH
_____ Discussion, TWE p. 623
_____ L3, Creating Pictographs, TWE p. 623

PRACTICE AND ASSESS
_____ Answers to Challenge and Pictoplay, TWE p. 623

CLOSE
_____ Close activity, TWE p. 623

* Teacher's Classroom Resources

Unit 23 Vocabulary and Spelling SE/TWE pp. 617–646

Teacher's Name _____ Date _____

Grade _____ Class(es) _____ Date(s) _____ M Tu W Th F

LESSON 23.3 *pp. 624–627*

FOCUS
LESSON OVERVIEW
Objective: To become familiar with roots, prefixes, and suffixes

_____ Bellringer and Motivating Activity, TWE p. 624

TEACH
Guided Practice
_____ L2, Brainstorming Prefixes, Suffixes, and Roots, TWE p. 625
_____ L1, Combining Word Parts, TWE p. 625
_____ Cultural Diversity, TWE p. 625
_____ Enabling Strategies: LEP, TWE p. 626
_____ Cross-reference: Spelling, TWE p. 627
_____ Enrichment and Extension, TWE p. 627

PRACTICE AND ASSESS
_____ Answers to Exercises 4 and 5, TWE p. 626
Independent Practice
_____ *Thinking and Study Skills*, pp. 9, 25–27 *
_____ *Vocabulary and Spelling Practice*, pp. 13, 21–26 *

CLOSE
_____ Close activity, TWE p. 627

┌─────────────────────────────┐
│ **• Homework Assignments •** │
│ _____ │
│ _____ │
│ _____ │
│ _____ │
│ _____ │
│ _____ │
│ _____ │
│ _____ │
│ _____ │
└─────────────────────────────┘

WORDWORKS 23.3 *p. 628*
LESSON OVERVIEW
Objective: To become familiar with compound words

TEACH
_____ Discussion, TWE p. 628
_____ L2, Making New Words, TWE p. 628
_____ Beyond the Classroom, TWE p. 628

PRACTICE AND ASSESS
_____ Answers to Challenge and Get It Together, TWE p. 628

CLOSE
_____ Close activity, TWE p. 628

* Teacher's Classroom Resources

Unit 23 Vocabulary and Spelling SE/TWE pp. 595–616

Teacher's Name _____ Date _____

Grade _____ Class(es) _____ Date(s) _____ M Tu W Th F

LESSON 23.4 pp. 629–630

FOCUS
LESSON OVERVIEW
Objective: To become familiar with synonyms and antonyms

_____ Bellringer, TWE p. 629

TEACH
Guided Practice
_____ L2, Writing Interesting Sentences, TWE p. 629
_____ Speaking and Listening, TWE p. 630

PRACTICE AND ASSESS
_____ Answers to Exercises 6 and 7, TWE p. 630

Independent Practice
_____ *Thinking and Study Skills*, pp. 9, 25–27 *
_____ *Vocabulary and Spelling Practice*, pp. 13, 21–26 *

CLOSE
_____ Close activity, TWE p. 630

┌─────────────────────────────┐
│ • *Homework Assignments* • │
│   │
│ _____   │
│ _____   │
│ _____   │
│ _____   │
│ _____   │
│ _____   │
│ _____   │
│ _____   │
└─────────────────────────────┘

WORDWORKS 23.4 p. 631
LESSON OVERVIEW
Objective: To understand the development of slang expressions

TEACH
_____ Discussion, TWE p. 631
_____ L2, Finding Slang Expressions, TWE p. 631
_____ Visual Thinking, TWE p. 631

PRACTICE AND ASSESS
_____ Evaluation Guidelines for Challenge and What's the Word, TWE p. 631

CLOSE
_____ Close activity, TWE p. 631

* Teacher's Classroom Resources

Unit 23 Vocabulary and Spelling SE/TWE pp. 617–646

Teacher's Name _____ Date _____

Grade _____ Class(es) _____ Date(s)_____ M Tu W Th F

LESSON 23.5 pp. 632–633

FOCUS
LESSON OVERVIEW
Objective: To become familiar with homonyms

_____ Bellringer, TWE p. 632

TEACH
Guided Practice
_____ L2, Inventing Homophone Riddles, TWE p. 632
_____ Technology Tip, TWE p. 633

PRACTICE AND ASSESS
_____ Answers to Exercise 8, TWE p. 633

Independent Practice
_____ *Thinking and Study Skills*, pp. 9, 25–27 *
_____ *Vocabulary and Spelling Practice*, pp. 13, 21–26 *

CLOSE
_____ Close activity, TWE p. 633

• Homework Assignments •

_____
_____
_____
_____
_____
_____
_____
_____

WORDWORKS 23.5 p. 634

LESSON OVERVIEW
Objective: To understand playful uses of homonyms

TEACH
_____ Discussion, TWE p. 634
_____ L3, Writing Dialogue, TWE p. 634
_____ Beyond the Classroom, TWE p. 634

PRACTICE AND ASSESS
_____ Answers to Challenge and Homophun, TWE p. 634

CLOSE
_____ Close activity, TWE p. 634

* Teacher's Classroom Resources

Unit 23 Vocabulary and Spelling *SE/TWE pp. 617–646*

Teacher's Name _____ Date _____

Grade _____ Class(es) _____ Date(s)_____ M Tu W Th F

LESSON 23.6 *pp. 635–638*

FOCUS
LESSON OVERVIEW
Objective: To become familiar with spelling rules

_____ Bellringer and Motivating Activity, TWE p. 635

TEACH
Guided Practice
_____ L2, Finding Examples of Spelling Rules, TWE p. 636
_____ Enabling Strategies: LEP, TWE p. 636
_____ Cross-reference: Vocabulary and Spelling, TWE p. 637
_____ Enrichment and Extension, TWE p. 637
_____ Speaking and Listening, TWE p. 638

PRACTICE AND ASSESS
_____ Answers to Exercises 9 and 10, TWE p. 638

Independent Practice
_____ *Thinking and Study Skills*, pp. 9, 25–27 *
_____ *Vocabulary and Spelling Practice*, pp. 13, 21–26 *

CLOSE
_____ Close activity, TWE p. 638

```
• Homework Assignments •

_____
_____
_____
_____
_____
_____
_____
_____
```

WORDWORKS 23.6 *p. 639*
LESSON OVERVIEW
Objective: To become familiar with the origins of silent letters in words

TEACH
_____ Discussion, TWE p. 639
_____ L1, Keeping a Notebook, TWE p. 639

PRACTICE AND ASSESS
_____ Answers to Challenge, TWE p. 639
_____ Evaluation Guidelines to Can You Speak Old English, TWE p. 639

CLOSE
_____ Close activity, TWE p. 639

* Teacher's Classroom Resources

Unit 23 Vocabulary and Spelling *SE/TWE pp. 617–646*

Teacher's Name _____ Date _____

Grade _____ Class(es) _____ Date(s)_____ M Tu W Th F

LESSON 23.7 *pp. 640–643*

FOCUS
LESSON OVERVIEW
Objective: To become familiar with spelling rules

_____ Bellringer and Motivating Activity, TWE p. 640

TEACH
Guided Practice
_____ Cross-reference: Usage, TWE p. 640
_____ L2, Listing Additional Examples, TWE p. 641
_____ Cross-reference: Usage, TWE p. 641
_____ Enabling Strategies: LEP, TWE p. 641
_____ L2, Guided Practice, TWE p. 642
_____ Cooperative Learning, TWE p. 642
_____ Visual Thinking, TWE p. 643

PRACTICE AND ASSESS
_____ Answers to Exercises 11 and 12, TWE p. 643

Independent Practice
_____ *Thinking and Study Skills,* pp. 9, 25–27 *
_____ *Vocabulary and Spelling Practice,* pp. 13, 21–26 *

LESSON 23.8 *pp. 644–646*

FOCUS
LESSON OVERVIEW
Objective: To become familiar with spelling problem words

_____ Bellringer and Motivating Activity, TWE p. 644

TEACH
Guided Practice
_____ L2, Spelling Commonly Misspelled Words, TWE p. 645
_____ L1, Using Pronunciation Guides, TWE p. 645
_____ Cooperative Learning, TWE p. 645
_____ Enabling Strategies: LEP, TWE p. 646

PRACTICE AND ASSESS
_____ Answers to Exercise 13, TWE p. 646

Independent Practice
_____ *Thinking and Study Skills,* pp. 9, 25–27 *
_____ *Vocabulary and Spelling Practice,* pp. 13, 21–26 *

* Teacher's Classroom Resources

CLOSE
_____ Close activity, TWE p. 643

• Homework Assignments •

_____
_____
_____
_____
_____
_____
_____
_____

CLOSE
_____ Close activity, TWE p. 646

Unit Assessment
_____ *Tests with Answer Key*
Unit 23 Mastery Test, pp. 91–92
_____ *Test Generator*
Unit 23 Mastery Test
You may wish to administer the
Unit 23 Mastery Test at this point.

Unit 24 Study Skills *SE/TWE 647–666*

Teacher's Name _____ Date _____

Grade _____ Class(es) _____ Date(s)_____ M Tu W Th F

LESSON 24.1 *pp. 647–648*

FOCUS
LESSON OVERVIEW
Objective: To become familiar with standard parts of a book

_____ Bellringer, TWE p. 647

TEACH
Guided Practice
_____ L2, Using Parts of a Book, TWE p. 647
_____ Connections Across the Curriculum: Science, TWE p. 648

PRACTICE AND ASSESS
_____ Answers to Exercise 1, TWE p. 648

Independent Practice
_____ *Speaking and Listening Activities*, pp. 10–11 *
_____ *Thinking and Study Skills*, pp. 2–4, 8, 18, 30–32, 34–36, 39–40 *

CLOSE
_____ Close activity, TWE p. 648

LESSON 24.2 *pp. 649–650*

FOCUS
LESSON OVERVIEW
Objective: To become familiar with different ways of reading

_____ Bellringer, TWE p. 649

TEACH
Guided Practice
_____ L2, Skimming Materials, TWE p. 649
_____ Visual Thinking, TWE p. 650

PRACTICE AND ASSESS
_____ Evaluation Guidelines to Exercise 2, TWE p. 650

Independent Practice
_____ *Thinking and Study Skills*, pp. 2–4, 8, 18, 30–32, 34–36, 39–40 *
_____ *Speaking and Listening Activities*, pp. 10–11 *

CLOSE
_____ Close activity, TWE p. 650

* Teacher's Classroom Resources

Unit Assessment
_____ *Tests with Answer Key*
Unit 24 Pretest, pp. 93–94
_____ *Test Generator*
Unit 24 Pretest
You may wish to administer the Unit 24 Pretest at this point.

• *Homework Assignments* •

_____
_____
_____
_____
_____
_____
_____
_____
_____

Unit 24 Study Skills *SE/TWE 647–666*

Teacher's Name _____ Date _____

Grade _____ Class(es) _____ Date(s)_____ M Tu W Th F

LESSON 24.3 *pp. 651–652*

FOCUS
LESSON OVERVIEW
Objective: To become familiar with writing summaries

_____ Bellringer, TWE p. 651

TEACH
Guided Practice
_____ L2, Practicing Summarizing, TWE p. 651
_____ Visual Thinking, TWE p. 652

PRACTICE AND ASSESS
_____ Evaluation Guidelines to Exercise 3, TWE p. 652

Independent Practice
_____ *Thinking and Study Skills*, pp. 2–4, 8, 18, 30–32, 34–36, 39–40 *
_____ *Speaking and Listening Activities*, pp. 10–11 *

CLOSE
_____ Close activity, TWE p. 652

• *Homework Assignments* •

_____
_____
_____
_____
_____
_____
_____
_____

LESSON 24.4 *pp. 653–655*

FOCUS
LESSON OVERVIEW
Objective: To learn how to make a study plan

_____ Bellringer and Motivating Activity, TWE p. 653

TEACH
Guided Practice
_____ L1, Learning to Identify Goals, TWE p. 654
_____ L3, Analyzing Interests, TWE p. 654
_____ Technology Tip, TWE p. 654
_____ Connections Across the Curriculum: History, TWE p. 655

PRACTICE AND ASSESS
_____ Evaluation Guidelines to Exercise 4, TWE p. 655

Independent Practice
_____ *Thinking and Study Skills*, pp. 2–4, 8, 18, 30–32, 34–36, 39–40 *
_____ *Speaking and Listening Activities*, pp. 10–11 *

CLOSE
_____ Close activity, TWE p. 655

* Teacher's Classroom Resources

Unit 24 Study Skills *SE/TWE 647–666*

Teacher's Name _____ Date _____

Grade _____ Class(es) _____ Date(s)_____ M Tu W Th F

LESSON 24.5 *pp. 656–657*

FOCUS
LESSON OVERVIEW
Objective: To become familiar with the SQ3R Method

_____ Bellringer, TWE p. 656

TEACH
Guided Practice
_____ L1, Using the Five W's and H, TWE p. 656
_____ Connections Across the Curriculum: Science, TWE p. 657

PRACTICE AND ASSESS
_____ Evaluation Guidelines to Exercise 5, TWE p. 657

Independent Practice
_____ *Thinking and Study Skills*, pp. 2–4, 8, 18, 30–32, 34–36, 39–40 *
_____ *Speaking and Listening Activities*, pp. 10–11 *

CLOSE
_____ Close activity, TWE p. 657

LESSON 24.6 *pp. 658–660*

FOCUS
LESSON OVERVIEW
Objective: To become familiar with taking notes and outlining

_____ Bellringer and Motivating Activity, TWE p. 658

TEACH
Guided Practice
_____ L2, Unscrambling Outlines, TWE p. 659
_____ Cooperative Learning, TWE p. 659
_____ Enabling Strategies: LEP, TWE p. 660

PRACTICE AND ASSESS
_____ Evaluation Guidelines to Exercise 6, TWE p. 660

Independent Practice
_____ *Thinking and Study Skills*, pp. 2–4, 8, 18, 30–32, 34–36, 39–40 *
_____ *Speaking and Listening Activities*, pp. 10–11 *

CLOSE
_____ Close activity, TWE p. 660

* Teacher's Classroom Resources

• Homework Assignments •

_____
_____
_____
_____
_____
_____
_____
_____

Unit 24 Study Skills *SE/TWE 647–666*

Teacher's Name _____ Date _____

Grade _____ Class(es) _____ Date(s)_____ M Tu W Th F

LESSON 24.7 *pp. 661–664*

FOCUS
LESSON OVERVIEW
Objective: To become familiar with graphic information

_____ Bellringer and Motivating Activity, TWE p. 661

TEACH
Guided Practice
_____ L2, Making a Bar Graph, TWE p. 662
_____ Enabling Strategies: LEP, TWE p. 662
_____ L3, Making a Table, TWE p. 663
_____ Speaking and Listening, TWE p. 663
_____ Enrichment and Extension, TWE p. 664

PRACTICE AND ASSESS
_____ Answers to Exercise 7, TWE p. 664

Independent Practice
_____ *Thinking and Study Skills*, pp. 2–4, 8, 18, 30–32, 34–36, 39–40 *
_____ *Speaking and Listening Activities*, pp. 10–11 *

LESSON 24.8 *pp. 665–666*

FOCUS
LESSON OVERVIEW
Objective: To become familiar with different ways of memorizing

_____ Bellringer, TWE p. 665

TEACH
Guided Practice
_____ L1, Using Mental Pictures, TWE p. 665
_____ Connections Across the Curriculum: History, TWE p. 666

PRACTICE AND ASSESS
_____ Evaluation Guidelines to Exercises 8 and 9, TWE p. 666

Independent Practice
_____ *Thinking and Study Skills*, pp. 2–4, 8, 18, 30–32, 34–36, 39–40 *
_____ *Speaking and Listening Activities*, pp. 10–11 *

CLOSE
_____ Close activity, TWE p. 666

* Teacher's Classroom Resources

CLOSE
_____ Close activity, TWE p. 664

• Homework Assignments •

_____
_____
_____
_____
_____
_____
_____
_____

Unit Assessment

_____ *Tests with Answer Key*
Unit 24 Mastery Test, pp. 95–96
_____ *Test Generator*
Unit 24 Mastery Test
You may wish to administer the
Unit 24 Mastery Test at this point.

Unit 25 Taking Tests *SE/TWE pp. 667–676*

Teacher's Name _____ Date _____

Grade _____ Class(es) _____ Date(s)_____ M Tu W Th F

LESSON 25.1 *pp. 667–668*

FOCUS
LESSON OVERVIEW
Objective: To become familiar with test-taking strategies

_____ Bellringer, TWE p. 667

TEACH
Guided Practice
_____ L2, Preparing with a Group, TWE p. 667
_____ Enabling Strategies: LEP, TWE p. 668

PRACTICE AND ASSESS
_____ Answers to Exercise 1, TWE p. 668

Independent Practice
_____ *Standardized Test Practice* *
_____ *Thinking and Study Skills*, pp. 41–42 *

CLOSE
_____ Close activity, TWE p. 668

LESSON 25.2 *pp. 669–672*

FOCUS
LESSON OVERVIEW
Objective: To become familiar with types of test items

_____ Bellringer and Motivating Activity, TWE p. 669

TEACH
Guided Practice
_____ L2, Reading Test Questions, TWE p. 670
_____ Enrichment and Extension, TWE p. 670
_____ Cross-reference: Study Skills, TWE p. 671
_____ Beyond the Classroom, TWE p. 671
_____ Enabling Strategies: LEP, TWE p. 672

PRACTICE AND ASSESS
_____ Answers to Matching Items, TWE p. 670
_____ Answers to Exercise 2, TWE p. 672

Independent Practice
_____ *Standardized Test Practice* *
_____ *Thinking and Study Skills*, pp. 41–42 *

Unit Assessment
_____ *Tests with Answer Key*
Unit 25 Pretest, pp. 97–98
_____ *Test Generator*
Unit 25 Pretest
You may wish to administer the
Unit 25 Pretest at this point.

• Homework Assignments •

_____
_____
_____
_____
_____
_____
_____
_____

CLOSE
_____ Close activity, TWE p. 672

* Teacher's Classroom Resources

Unit 25 Taking Tests *SE/TWE pp. 667–676*

Teacher's Name _____ Date _____

Grade _____ Class(es) _____ Date(s)_____ M Tu W Th F

LESSON 25.3 *pp. 673–676*

FOCUS
LESSON OVERVIEW
Objective: To become familiar with types of questions in standardized tests

_____ Bellringer and Motivating Activity, TWE p. 673

TEACH
Guided Practice
_____ L1, Searching for Key Words, TWE p. 674
_____ Cross-reference: Vocabulary and Spelling, TWE p. 674
_____ Cross-reference: Vocabulary and Spelling, TWE p. 674
_____ Enabling Strategies: LEP, TWE p. 674
_____ L3, Practicing Analogies, TWE p. 675
_____ Cross-reference: Usage, TWE p. 675
_____ Cooperative Learning, TWE p. 675
_____ Technology Tip, TWE p. 676

PRACTICE AND ASSESS
_____ Answers to Exercise 3, TWE p. 676

Independent Practice
_____ *Standardized Test Practice* *
_____ *Thinking and Study Skills*, pp. 41–42 *

CLOSE
_____ Close activity, TWE p. 676

* Teacher's Classroom Resources

• *Homework Assignments* •

_____
_____
_____
_____
_____
_____
_____
_____

Unit Assessment

_____ *Tests with Answer Key*
Unit 25 Mastery Test, pp. 90–100
_____ *Test Generator*
Unit 25 Mastery Test
You may wish to administer the Unit 25 Mastery Test at this point.

Unit 26 Listening and Speaking *SE/TWE pp. 677–698*

Teacher's Name _____ Date _____

Grade _____ Class(es) _____ Date(s)_____ M Tu W Th F

LESSON 26.1 *pp. 677–681*

FOCUS
LESSON OVERVIEW
Objective: To learn how to listen

_____ Bellringer and Motivating Activity, TWE p. 677

TEACH
Guided Practice
_____ L2, Listening for Emotional Words, Opinions, and Facts, TWE p. 678
_____ L1, Writing Facts and Opinions, TWE p. 678
_____ Cross-reference: Usage, TWE p. 678
_____ Enabling Strategies: LEP, TWE p. 678
_____ L2, Analyzing Words Used in Commercials, TWE p. 679
_____ Cross-reference: Writing, TWE p. 679
_____ Speaking and Listening, TWE p. 679
_____ L2, Finding Hidden Messages, TWE p. 680
_____ Visual Thinking, TWE p. 680
_____ Cooperative Learning, TWE p. 681

PRACTICE AND ASSESS
_____ Evaluation Guidelines to Exercise 1, TWE p. 681

Independent Practice
_____ *Speaking and Listening Activities*, pp. 6–8, 12–13, 16–24 *
_____ *Thinking and Study Skills*, pp. 33–34 *

LESSON 26.2 *pp. 682–685*

FOCUS
LESSON OVERVIEW
Objective: To become familiar with interviews

_____ Bellringer and Motivating Activity, TWE p. 682

TEACH
Guided Practice
_____ L2, Practicing Interviewing, TWE p. 683
_____ Cross-reference: Writing, TWE p. 683
_____ Cross-reference: Writing, TWE p. 683
_____ Technology Tip, TWE p. 683
_____ L1, Choosing Subjects, TWE p. 684
_____ Enabling Strategies: LEP, TWE p. 684
_____ Beyond the Classroom, TWE p. 685

PRACTICE AND ASSESS
_____ Evaluation Guidelines to Exercise 2, TWE p. 685

Unit Assessment

_____ *Tests with Answer Key*
Unit 26 Pretest, pp. 101–102
_____ *Test Generator*
Unit 26 Pretest
You may wish to administer the
Unit 26 Pretest at this point.

CLOSE
_____ Close activity, TWE p. 681

• *Homework Assignments* •

_____

_____

_____

_____

_____

_____

_____

_____

Independent Practice
_____ *Speaking and Listening Activities*,
pp. 6–8, 12–13, 16–24 *
_____ *Thinking and Study Skills*, pp.
33–34 *

CLOSE
_____ Close activity, TWE p. 685

* Teacher's Classroom Resources

Unit 26 Listening and Speaking SE/TWE pp. 677–698

Teacher's Name _____ Date _____

Grade _____ Class(es) _____ Date(s)_____ M Tu W Th F

LESSON 26.3 pp. 686–690

FOCUS
LESSON OVERVIEW
Objective: To become familiar with speaking informally

_____ Bellringer and Motivating Activity, TWE p. 686

TEACH
Guided Practice
_____ L2, Making Introductions, TWE p. 687
_____ Cross-reference: Speaking and Listening, TWE p. 687
_____ Enabling Strategies: LEP, TWE p. 687
_____ L2, Practicing Speaking in a Group, TWE p. 688
_____ L3, Pacing Conversation, TWE p. 688
_____ Technology Tip, TWE p. 688
_____ L1, Working Through a Process, TWE p. 689
_____ Cross-reference: Writing, TWE p. 689
_____ Beyond the Classroom, TWE p. 689

PRACTICE AND ASSESS
_____ Evaluation Guidelines to Exercises 3 and 4, TWE p. 690

Independent Practice
_____ *Speaking and Listening Activities*, pp. 6–8, 12–13, 16–24 *
_____ *Thinking and Study Skills*, pp. 33–34 *

LESSON 26.4 PP. 691–693

FOCUS
LESSON OVERVIEW
Objective: To become familiar with speaking orally

_____ Bellringer and Motivating Activity, TWE p. 691

TEACH
Guided Practice
_____ L2, Identifying the Difference Between Oral and Written Reports, TWE p. 692
_____ Cross-reference: Writing, TWE p. 692
_____ Cross-reference: Writing, TWE p. 692
_____ Technology Tip, TWE p. 692
_____ Enabling Strategies: LEP, TWE p. 693

PRACTICE AND ASSESS
_____ Evaluation Guidelines to Exercise 5, TWE p. 693

CLOSE
_____ Close activity, TWE p. 690

• Homework Assignments •

_____
_____
_____
_____
_____
_____
_____
_____

Independent Practice
_____ *Speaking and Listening Activities*, pp. 6–8, 12–13, 16–24 *
_____ *Thinking and Study Skills*, pp. 33–34 *

CLOSE
_____ Close activity, TWE p. 693

* Teacher's Classroom Resources

Unit 26 Listening and Speaking *SE/TWE pp. 677–698*

Teacher's Name _____ Date _____

Grade _____ Class(es) _____ Date(s)_____ M Tu W Th F

LESSON 26.5 *pp. 694–698*

FOCUS
LESSON OVERVIEW
Objective: To become familiar with speaking formally

_____ Bellringer and Motivating Activity, TWE p. 694

TEACH
Guided Practice
_____ L2, Preparing a Speech, TWE p. 695
_____ Cross-reference: Writing, TWE p. 695
_____ Enabling Strategies: LEP, TWE p. 695
_____ L2, Using Notes or Scripts, TWE p. 696
_____ Speaking and Listening, TWE p. 696
_____ L3, Learning from Accomplished Speakers, TWE p. 697
_____ Cooperative Learning, TWE p. 697
_____ Technology Tip, TWE p. 698

PRACTICE AND ASSESS
_____ Answers to Exercise 6, TWE p. 698

Independent Practice
_____ *Speaking and Listening Activities*, pp. 6–8, 12–13, 16–24 *
_____ *Thinking and Study Skills*, pp. 33–34 *

CLOSE
_____ Close activity, TWE p. 698

* Teacher's Classroom Resources

• Homework Assignments •

_____
_____
_____
_____
_____
_____
_____
_____

Unit Assessment

_____ *Tests with Answer Key*
Unit 26 Mastery Test, pp. 103–104
_____ *Test Generator*
Unit 26 Mastery Test
You may wish to administer the Unit 26 Mastery Test at this point.